VEGETARIAN
& VEGAN GUIDE TO
BRISTOL
& BATH

Includes Bradford-on-Avon,
Clevedon and
Weston-Super-Mare

Viva! Vegetarian & Vegan Guide to Bristol & Bath

ISBN 978-0-9547216-8-8
1st edition, June 2007

Compiled and edited by: Angie Greenaway

Published by: Viva!, 8 York Court, Wilder Street, Bristol
BS2 8QH T: 0117 944 1000 F: 0117 924 4646
E: info@viva.org.uk W: www.viva.org.uk

Designed by: The Ethical Graphic Design Company
www.ethicalgraphicdesign.co.uk

Acknowledgements

Thanks to Rob for the immense moral and practical support
he has given me, both in producing this guide and generally
day-to-day. I'd be lost without you! Also to the Viva! team
for all their hard work in trying to bring about real change
and, through education and helping people to switch to a
veggie diet, saving the lives of millions of farmed animals.
It's a privilege working with you all.

Contents

Weston-Super-Mare

190 Other

Please note

Establishments are listed alphabetically and in the case of
Bristol and Clevedon, are also broken down further to help
the reader locate them, and nearby businesses, more readily.
To find specific places, please refer to the index on page 203.

Although great care has been taken to ensure that the
information in this guide is correct and up-to-date, Viva!
accepts no responsibility for any changes as menus,
opening times, ownership of establishments are obviously
subject to change.

Although not listed in the guide, a number of national chains
provide good veggie options. For example, Caffé Nero, Costa
and Starbucks all provide soya milk and Wetherspoons serves
veggie burgers that are vegan too. Co-op stores clearly label
their products – including a wide selection of wines –
vegetarian and vegan, as well as cruelty-free. Where you can,
it's good to support the independents but it's nice to know
that you're catered for by the big boys too!

A quick guide to 100% veggie and the most veggie-friendly places

100% Vegan

Bristol:	Aromafoods	108
	Café Kino	103

100% Veggie

Bath:	Demuths Restaurant	127
	The Metropolitan Café	135
	The Bell	124
	Harvest	150
	London Road Food Co-op	151
	Lush	151
	The Porter	138
Bristol:	Arches Hotel	18
	Aromafoods	108
	The Base	19
	The Big Banana Juice Bar	24+30
	Café Kino	103
	Café Maitreya	81
	The Falafel King	35
	Fruit Sticks	28
	Harvest	76
	Lush	27
	One Stop Thali Café	91
	Riverside Garden Centre Café	98

Most veggie-friendly places (more than 75%)

Key to services

- Soya milk
- Free-range eggs
- Veggie cheese
- Fair-trade items
- Veggie/vegan alcohol
- Licensed
- Bring your own
- Caters for special diets
- Avoid GM
- Organic where possible
- All you can eat
- Counter service
- Delivery
- Table service
- Take-Away
- Cheques accepted
- Major credit cards accepted
- Booking advised
- Disabled access/facilities
- Parking
- Dogs allowed
- Viva! discount

Your comments welcome

If you have visited or know of an establishment that you think should be included in the next edition of the *Vegetarian & Vegan Guide to Bristol & Bath*, please contact Viva! (see opposite for details).

About Viva!

Publisher of the *Vegetarian & Vegan Guide to Bristol & Bath*

Viva! is Europe's leading vegetarian and vegan campaigning group. It actively works, through its offices in the UK and Poland, to both highlight the plight of farmed animals and promote the benefits – to animals, the environment and ourselves – of a vegetarian/vegan diet.

For further information about Viva!'s work, please contact us at: 8 York Court, Wilder Street, Bristol BS2 8QH
Tel: 0117 944 1000 Email: info@viva.org.uk www.viva.org.uk

© Heather Watson/Alamy

Viva! discounts available

Through our Supporters' Discount Scheme, Viva! supporters can benefit from money-saving offers year-round at a variety of veggie-friendly businesses throughout the UK (and further afield) including guest houses, hotels, restaurants, cafés and health food stores.

If you would like to become a Viva! supporter and save £££s by taking advantage of this wonderful scheme, complete and return the join form on the inside back cover of this guide, call us today on 0117 944 1000 or visit our website www.viva.org.uk where you can join online. And just think, not only are you getting more for less when holidaying, eating out or shopping, but you are helping to save animals' lives at the same time by supporting Viva!'s work!

Bath
114 Apsley House Hotel 10% on bookings Mon-Fri only
129 The Hole in the Wall 10%
140 The Rajpoot 10%

Bristol
49 Oppo3 Music Coffee House 10%
94 Pippin Harris 10% (excl fruit, veg and cheese)
31 Royce Rolls Wholefood Café 10%
93 Seven Generations 5%

Glastonbury
195 The Bridget Healing Centre 10% off treatments incl
    Reiki, Indian Head Massage, Reflexology
194 The Lightship 3 nights for the price of 2 (Mon-Thurs)
195 The Wholefood Store 10%

Bristol

Bristol's a diverse and colourful city offering visitors and residents alike a whole spectrum of things to do and places to see whatever the weather. Home to a whole host of internationally recognised festivals for all the family throughout the year, you can take your pick from such gems as the colourful Balloon Fiesta (August) and International Festival of Kites & Air Creations (September) to the Soil Association Organic Food Festival (September) and Wildscreen Festival (October). It's also home to the annual Bristol Vegan Fayre (June). Historical attractions include Isambard Kingdom Brunel's world-renowned Clifton Suspension Bridge and SS Great Britain. There's also a selection of parks and green spaces across the city, a diverse range of pubs, bars and restaurants to suit all tastes, not to mention a myriad of shops ranging from high street stores to quirky independents and vintage boutiques. Bristol really does offer something for everyone. And veggies and vegans will have no trouble finding somewhere to eat to suit their budget. So go forth and explore… Bristol-fashion!

Clifton Suspension Bridge

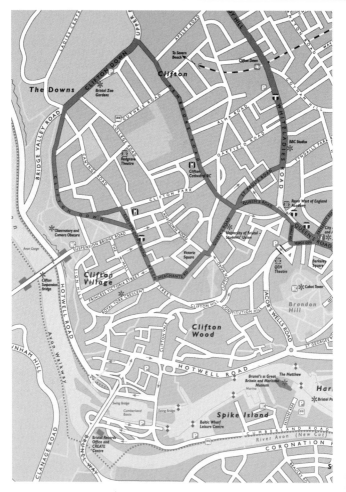

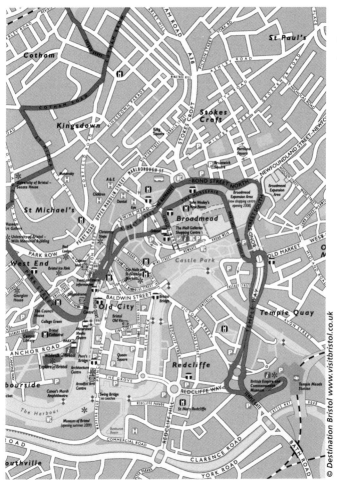

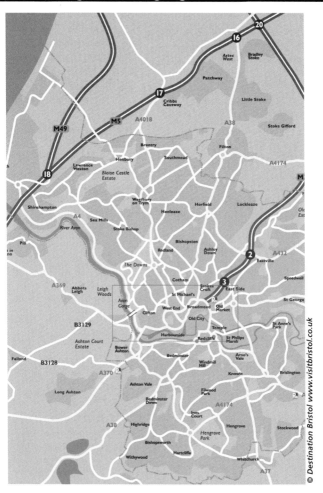

Top tourist attractions

Clifton Suspension Bridge

Suspension Bridge Road, Clifton, Bristol BS8 3PA
Tel: 0117 974 4664 www.clifton_suspension_bridge.co.uk
Open: Year round
Isambard Kingdom Brunel never got to see his creation, his first major commission, which was finished in 1864. Its spectacular setting on the cliffs of the Avon Gorge has made it the symbol of Bristol. Guided tours are available by arrangement. You can also walk along the nearby Downs and get a great view of the bridge and Bristol – as well as spot wildlife, from bugs and butterflies to kestrels and peregrine falcons.

SS Great Britain

Great Western Dockyard, Gas Ferry Road, Bristol BS1 6TY
Tel: 0117 926 0680 www.ssgreatbritain.org
Open: April-October: 10am-5.30pm, November-March: 10am-4.30pm
Tickets: £8.95 Adult, £6.95 Concession, £4.95 Child (under 4s free)
Built and launched in 1843, Isambard Kingdom Brunel's maritime masterpiece was the world's first ocean-going, propeller driven iron ship. After a life as a luxury liner, she was used as a troop ship, cargo vessel and floating warehouse after being abandoned in the Falkland Islands in 1937. She was salvaged in 1970, towed back to Bristol and has now been restored to her former glory. Viva! held its 10th anniversary dinner on board, back in October 2004, in the beautiful dining room. Well worth a trip.

Tourist information

Bristol Tourist Information Point

Bristol City Museum & Art Gallery, Queens Road,
Bristol BS8 1RL
Tel: 0906 711 2191 (50p/minute)

Bristol Visitor Information

Bristol Empire & Commonwealth Museum, next to
Temple Meads Railway Station, Bristol
Open: Monday-Sunday 10am-5pm

Bristol Tourist Information at the Travel Bristol Centre

11 Colston Avenue, Bristol BS1 4UB
Tel: 0906 711 2191 (50p/minute)
Open: Monday-Friday 10.30am-5.30pm, Saturday 10am-1pm

Bristol Visitor Information Centre

Wildwalk At Bristol, Anchor Road, Harbourside,
Bristol BS1 5DB
Tel: 0906 711 2191 (50p/minute)
Open: Monday-Friday 10am-5pm, Saturday-Sunday and
School Holidays 10am-6pm

Places to stay

Arches Hotel (3 Diamond) ⬤⬤🕭🅶🕭🕭

132 Cotham Brow, Cotham, Bristol BS6 6AE
Tel: 0117 924 7398 www.arches-hotel.co.uk

Open: Year round, except Christmas

Number of rooms: 9; **En-suite**: 4

Cost: £30.00-£45.00 (single) and £45.00-£60.50 (double) per night

Veggie breakfast: Cereals; Warm croissants/toast; Choice of five cooked breakfasts: for example, free-range egg, sausages, tomato & toast

Vegan breakfast: Cereals; Warm toast; Cooked breakfast: beans, sausages, tomato & toast

Small, friendly vegetarian Victorian hotel that's green as well as meat-free. You can be sure of a good night's sleep, whatever the season, as all bedrooms are kitted out with an ioniser to remove dust and pollen. Perfect for allergy sufferers.

Basca House (3 Star) ⬤🕭🕭

19 Broadway Road, Bishopston, Bristol BS7 8ES
Tel: 0117 942 2182

Open: Year round, except Christmas and New Year

Number of rooms: 4; **En-suite**: 0

Cost: £28.00 (single) and £46.00 (twin) per room/per night

Veggie breakfast: Fresh fruit; Cereals; Cooked breakfast

Vegan breakfast: Available on request

Elegant Victorian house in quiet tree-lined road, well located close to the A38. Beautifully restored throughout and each of the four guest rooms is large and spacious. Rated as providing an "Excellent veggie/vegan spread for breakfast".

The Base ⊙⊙⊙⊙⊙⊙⊙⊙⊙

67 Stonebridge Park, Upper Eastville, Bristol BS5 6RP
Tel: 0117 902 3603 www.thebase.vg

Open: Year round
Number of rooms: 1; **En-suite**: 1
Cost: £39.00-£42.00 (single) and £60.00-£64.00 (double)
per night
Views: Over garden and viaduct
Veggie breakfast: Veggie fry-up with Indian pakorah, bagels
and croissants; Pancakes with choice of toppings; Yoghurts
and muesli topped with fruit & maple syrup, Porridge
Vegan breakfast: Vegan fry-up with sausages & tofu
*100% veggie, warm and welcoming family home offering a
completely refurbished ground floor with a double en-suite
and adjoining spacious lounge with doors opening to the
pergola and south facing garden. With its own entrance, you
can enjoy a real home from home. Evening meals (£10, with
a glass of wine) and health/beauty treatments (Shiatsu
healing massage or foot treatment) are also available.*

The Coach House ⊙⊙⊙

Bristol Road, Hambrook, Bristol BS16 1RY
Tel: 0117 956 6901 www.bristolcoachhouse.co.uk

Open: Year round
Number of rooms: 14; **En-suite**: 14
Cost: £40.00 single, £54.00 two people sharing, £70.00 three
people sharing, £75.00 four people sharing
Views: Five rooms have very picturesque rural views, two
rooms overlooking courtyard
Veggie breakfast: Continental breakfast: cereals, jams, fruit,
croissants, cheese spread, yoghurts; Cooked breakfast:
poached, scrambled or fried egg, fresh or tinned tomatoes,

beans, toast

Vegan breakfast: Available on request

An 18th century Grade II listed guest house, formerly a coaching house, set in the picturesque village of Hambrook, also a conservation area, and only a mile from Bristol Parkway station. With courtyard garden and off-road private parking.

Elm Tree Cottage ⊖ ⦵ ⦿ ⦾ ⦿ ⓟ

Jacklands Bridge, Tickenham, Nailsea, Bristol BS21 6SQ
Tel: 01275 866484 www.aspecialplacetostay.co.uk

Open: Year round

Number of rooms: 4; **En-suite**: 4

Cost: £40.00/£45.00 (single) and £55.00/£60.00 (double/twin) per room per night

Views: Some rooms with views across fields towards Nailsea and the Mendips

Veggie breakfast: Porridge; Pancakes; Cooked breakfast

Vegan breakfast: Cooked breakfast

Charming and original country cottage B&B set in the conservation area of Tickenham Hill, just eight miles from Bristol. Guests can blow out the cobwebs with a walk in the adjoining Towerhouse Woods, ancient woodland owned and managed by the Woodland Trust. Elm Tree Cottage provides excellent hospitality and a friendly and efficient service, with specially prepared veggie and vegan breakfasts.

Don't forget to mention the Vegetarian & Vegan Guide to Bristol & Bath when making an enquiry or booking!

The Grey House ⊙⊙⊙⊙⊙

The Common, Patchway, Bristol BS34 6AL
Tel: 01454 852820 www.grey-house.biz

Open: Year round
Number of rooms: 11; **En-suite**: 6
Cost: £35.00-£38.00 (single) and £52.00 (double) per room per night
Views: Some rooms overlooking garden
Veggie breakfast: Cooked breakfast: Veggie fingers, hash browns, beans, tomatoes & mushrooms
Vegan breakfast: Cooked breakfast: Beans, tomatoes & mushrooms

B&B located six miles from city centre and two miles from the Cribbs Causeway shopping complex. Variety of rooms, including family rooms which also helpfully have shared use of a kitchen.

Well Cottage ⊙⊙⊙⊙⊙

The Common, Patchway, Bristol BS34 6AL
Tel: 01454 855767 www.wellcottagebristol.co.uk

Open: Year round
Number of rooms: 5; **En-suite**: 2 plus 2 bed cottage
Cost: From £30.00 single, £45.00 twin/double standard, £50.00 twin en-suite, £60.00 family
Views: Limited
Veggie breakfast: Continental breakfast: cereals, muffins, bread, jams, yoghurt, cereal bars, fruit
Vegan breakfast: As above but without dairy products and soya milk – please advise when booking

Well Cottage provides B&B and self-catering accommodation in a converted stable block and barn. There are two kitchens for guests to use and all bedrooms are located at ground floor level. Off-street parking available.

Westfield House (4 Red Diamond) ⊖⊘⊗⊗⊗⊘⊘⊘

37 Stoke Hill, Stoke Bishop, Bristol BS9 1LQ
Tel: 0117 962 6119 www.westfieldhouse.net

Open: Year round
Number of rooms 3; **En-suite**: 3
Cost: From £59.00-£90.00 (single) and £69.00-£104.00 (double) per room per night
Views: Over garden
Veggie breakfast: Exotic fruit salad; Greek yoghurt & honey; Omelette
Vegan breakfast: Available on request

Friendly family-run guest house situated in 2.5 acres of private gardens and just 10 minutes drive from the city centre. A haven for wildlife – owls, badgers, falcons and hedgehogs have all been spotted in the grounds.

Woodstock Guest House (3 Star) ⊘⊘

534 Bath Road, Brislington, Bristol BS4 3JZ
Tel: 0117 987 1613 www.homestead.com/wstock

Open: Year round, except Christmas and New Year
Number of rooms: 5; **En-suite**: 3
Cost: From £35.00 (single) and £60.00 (double) per room per night
Veggie breakfast: Available on request

Woodstock dates back to 1890 and was built in the grounds of Arnos Manor. It's just one mile from the city centre and has a lovely garden with patio and ornamental pond where you can relax. Also advertises itself as gay-friendly.

City centre: Broadmead
Places to eat

The Big Banana Juice Bar 😀 🅐

15-29 Union Street, Carrefour Gym, Bristol BS1 2DF
Tel: 0117 927 3274 www.thebigbananajuicebar.co.uk

Opening times: Monday-Friday 7am-9pm, Saturday 8am-6pm and Sunday 10am-6pm

Veggie rating: 100% Vegetarian; 73% Vegan

Average cost: Juices £1.80-£3.30/Boosters £1.00/Wheatgrass £1.75

Long-established in Bristol, the Big Banana has spread its wings to Union Street and provides gym visitors, as well as passing shoppers, with top quality liquid and energy-giving refreshment. You can power up a regular juice by adding a booster of spirulina or essential omega oils (plant-based of course). Also at St Nicholas Market (see page 30).

Juice Hub (Juice & Smoothie Bar) 😀 🐄 😀 🅐 ✪ ✪

The Prudential Buildings, Wine Street, Bristol BS1 2PH
Tel: 0870 626 0344 www.juicehub.com

Opening times: Monday-Friday 7.30am-5pm, Saturday 9.30am-5pm and Sunday 11am-5pm

Veggie rating: 63% Vegetarian; 34% Vegan

Music/vibe: Ambient/world

Average cost: Juices/smoothies £2.50

Opposite Castle Green and next to Tesco, Juice Hub is a relative new kid on the block. But, unlike some juice bars, you can stay and enjoy your smoothie or juice (not to mention hot panini, organic porridge, healthy sweet treat, sandwich, salad or even tea or coffee) either al fresco or

inside. Sadly none of the 'solid' food is vegan but any dairy-based smoothies can be replaced with soya milk on request.

La Grotta (Italian Restaurant) ⭕ 🌐 🚻 💷 📷 ♻

> *7 Union Street, Bristol BS1 2DD*
> *Tel: 0117 929 0466*

Opening times: Monday-Thursday 11.30am-2.30pm and 5-10.30pm, Friday 11.30am-2.30pm and 5-11.30pm, Saturday 11.30am-midnight and Sunday 5-10.30pm

Veggie rating: 40% Vegetarian; 10% Vegan

Music/vibe: Italian

Average cost: Starters £4.95/Main dishes £6.00-£7.00

Cosy family-owned restaurant which for the past 20 years has been serving up authentic Italian fare. A great place to come for group bookings, the Papa Lounge downstairs also has its own dance floor, great for working off those calories! And you'll be surprised by the choice – it's not just the usual pasta and pizza dishes on offer. There's some great alternatives, such as Riso Cashew (rice, cashew nuts, mushrooms, courgettes, onion and garlic made into croquettes, deep fried and topped with tomato sauce) and Gnocchi (potato and pasta dumplings in tomato sauce topped with melted cheese) and they're more than happy to accommodate special dietary requests. Much loved and a firm favourite with its regulars.

Shakeaway 🔵 🆂🅳 🔵 🆃🅰

8-10 The Arcade, Bristol BS1 3JA
Tel: 0117 922 1991 www.shakeaway.com

Opening times: Monday-Friday 9am-6pm, Saturday 9am-6.30pm and Sunday 11am-5.30pm

Veggie rating: 38% Vegetarian; 25% Vegan

Average cost: Regular shake £2.50/Large £3.60 (add 99p/£1.49 for organic soya milk/ice cream)

Just by Starbucks and Costa, Shakeaway is spacious and inviting and is likely to lure away many of the coffee giants' punters. There is a large menu, with vegetarian and vegan items clearly marked and soya milk and ice cream are available for an extra charge. With lots of weird and wonderful ingredients to form the flavour of your shake, this place is a particular hit with the kids. Also in Bath (see page 142).

Shake King 🔵 🔵 🆃🅰

106 Horsefair, Bristol BS1 3JX
Tel: 0117 302 0029 www.shakeking.com

Opening times: Monday-Saturday 10am-6pm and Sunday 11am-5pm

Veggie rating: 25% Vegetarian; 15% Vegan

Average cost: £2.50/£3.20 (add 99p for soya milk/ice cream)

Apparently, Shake King is Bristol's 'original shake bar' so it's clearly paved the way for those that have since followed in its footsteps. Their flagship store, the bar serves up its shakes in a clean, clutter-free environment.

Shops

Holland & Barrett

83 The Horsefair, Bristol BS1 3JP
Tel: 0117 929 3170 www.hollandandbarrett.com
Opening times: Monday-Saturday 9am-5.30pm and Sunday 10am-4pm
There's a lot packed into this store, especially the chiller section which is full of take-away pies and pasties as well as drinks, soya yoghurts, dairy-free cheeses, Cheatin' slices, sausages and more. The freezer section also has a great choice of vegetarian and vegan products.

Lush

73 Broadmead, Bristol BS1 3DX
Tel: 0117 925 7582 www.lush.co.uk
Opening times: Monday-Saturday 9.30am-5.30pm and Sunday 11am-5pm
I love Lush and there is something about the experience of shopping there that is so different to anywhere else. Just follow your nose and saunter in and let your eyes be drawn to the products you like. The hardest thing is what to choose! If you're stuck just ask any of the staff – all are enthusiastically helpful. Lush products make great presents – I only wish I got more!! Also in Bath (see page 151).

Superdrug

39-43 Broadmead, Bristol BS1 3EU
Tel: 0117 927 9928

Opening times: Monday-Saturday 8.30am-5.30pm and Sunday 11am-5pm

Although there seems to be more and more veggie body and hair care products, the one area where vegans really struggle – especially on the high street – is trying to find cruelty-free and animal-free cosmetics. Thank heaven for Barry M, available through Superdrug, whose entire make-up range is vegetarian. It's not all vegan so steer clear of the Foundation Crème, Shimmering Body Crème, Translucent Compact, Natural Dazzle Compact, Shimmering Eye and Lip Crayon, Lip Paint, Lip Gloss and Mascara.

City centre: The Galleries
Places to eat

Fruit Sticks

The Galleries, Broadmead, Bristol
www.fruitonastick.com

Veggie rating: 100% Vegetarian; 66% Vegan

Average cost: Fruit sticks £2.00/Juices & smoothies £2.50/Fruit pots £2.90

Situated on the first floor of The Galleries shopping centre, Fruit Sticks serves up fruity fresh and healthy drinks and snacks from its eye-catching kiosk. Kids will particularly love the fruit sticks – chunks of different fruits skewered on to a bamboo stick – and you can make up your own juice combos.

Shops

Dr & Herbs

Unit BG14, The Galleries, Broadmead,
Bristol BS1 3XB
Tel: 0117 922 7888 www.drherbs.co.uk

Opening times: Monday-Saturday 9am-6pm and Sunday
11am-5pm

With over 60 shops and 300 qualified doctors to their name,
Dr & Herbs has brought traditional Chinese medicine,
Chinese herbs and acupuncture to the high street. Following
a consultation, a recommended treatment or course of herbs
will be prescribed.

GNC

Unit BG5, The Galleries, Broadmead, Bristol BS1 3XB
Tel: 0117 925 4270 www.gnc.co.uk

Opening times: Monday-Saturday 9am-5.30pm and Sunday
11am-5pm

Limited on food items, focusing more on supplements, GNC
does offer quite a good range of body and hair care
products, including hair dyes and natural therapies.

Herbmedic (Herbs & Acupuncture)

GW7, The Galleries, Broadmead, Bristol BS1 3DX
Tel: 0117 929 8588 www.herbmedic.co.uk

Opening times: Monday-Saturday 9.30am-5.30pm and
Sunday 11am-5pm

One of 72 branches nationwide, Herbmedic using Chinese
Herbal Therapy, Acupuncture, Cupping Therapy, Acupressure,
Ear Candle, Allergy Testing and Moxibustion (no, I'd never

heard of it either – but it's the application of mild heat to the body using glowing Moxa wool, which is in fact a finely chopped herb). Consultation with a qualified practitioner is free and treatments range from £5.00 per bag of dry herbs up to £35.00 for Acupressure/Allergy Testing.

Julian Graves
The Galleries, Broadmead, Bristol BS1 3XB
Tel: 0117 922 0664 www.juliangraves.co.uk
Opening times: Monday-Saturday 9am-6pm and Sunday 11am-5pm
Packed with all sorts of nuts and other nibbles, this is a good place to grab a bag of something to keep you going for the journey home. There's also boxes of sweet treats, good for gifts and various ingredients for cooking. (I've just been the lucky recipient of some yummy coconut covered Turkish delight – highly recommended!!)

City centre: Corn Street & St Nicholas Market
Places to eat

The Big Banana Juice Bar ● ⓐ
Unit 21, The Glass Arcade, St Nicholas Market, Corn Street, Bristol BS1 1LG
Tel: 0117 927 3274 www.thebigbananajuicebar.co.uk
Opening times: Monday-Friday 7.30am-5pm and Saturday 8am-5pm
Veggie rating: 100% Vegetarian; 73% Vegan

Average cost: £1.80-£3.30 juices/£1.00 boosters/£1.75 wheatgrass

Just outside the entrance to St Nicholas Market by Royce Rolls, you can spot The Big Banana by its large trays of fresh vibrant wheatgrass. As well as running a juice bar at local events, these guys also preach what they practice, taking the principles of juicing into schools and teaching the kids how and why to do it. Also in Union Street, Bristol (see page 24).

Revival Café ⊜◯⊛◐⊝⊞

    56 Corn Street, Bristol BS1 1JG
    Tel: 0117 930 4008

Opening times: Monday-Friday 8am-5pm, Saturday 8.30am-5pm and Sunday 10am-4pm
Veggie rating: 40% Vegetarian; 5% Vegan
Music/vibe: Chilled, ambient
Average cost: Eat-in: Soups, Sandwiches, Paninis £3.25-£3.95/Salads £5.50/Jackets £4.00

A popular hang-out, with plenty of seating upstairs as well as outdoors, Revival provides a good veggie choice of sandwiches, panini, pizzas and cakes (all of which are veggie) for its customers.

Royce Rolls Wholefood Café
⊜◯⊛⊛⊛⊛⊛◯◯⊞⊛⊘

    Corn Exchange, St Nicholas Market, Bristol BS1 1JQ
    Tel: 07791 523014

Opening times: Monday-Friday 7.30am-4pm and Saturday 9.30am-5pm
Veggie rating: 95% Vegetarian; 20% Vegan
Music/vibe: World
Average cost: £1.00-£2.50

Royce Rolls is something of an institution so it's not surprising that it's the oldest (virtually) veggie café outside of London, having been in business since 1979 when probably a lot of this guide's readers won't even have been born! Always busy and a much-used meeting place, you're spoilt for choice with a wide selection of rolls, pies and cakes on offer. Shame that there's still some fish on the menu but you can't have everything! Favourites include the Sausage Salad Roll and Australian Crunch, both vegan.

Spice Up Your Life (Punjabi) ●

    7 Exchange Avenue, Bristol BS1 1LJ
    Tel: 0117 914 4448
Opening times: Monday-Saturday 9.30am-5pm
Veggie rating: 70% Vegetarian & Vegan
Average cost: £3.50 for two veggie dishes and rice
Right next to Royce Rolls (see above), Spice Up Your Life regularly dishes up plates of tasty veggie fare at great value-for-money. On a nice day, you can sit outside and while away your lunch break watching the world go by or when the weather's not so nice inside with the Royce Rolls' crowd.

City centre: Harbourside & Docks
Places to eat

A Fair Cup ● ⏱ ● 🆚

    www.afaircup.com
Opening times: Monday-Friday 6.30am-7.30pm and Saturday 8am-6pm
Run from a kiosk on the central promenade between The

Hippodrome and Baldwin Street, A Fair Cup serves fair-trade coffee as well as a selection of snacks and other drinks, including Big Banana juices. All coffee used is grown in Sumatra by a co-operative in the Gayo Highlands, the first and still only collaboration of its kind in Indonesia.

Blue Pepper Café/Take Out
⊜⊙⊗⊙⊙Ⓥ⑤Ⓜ⊙⊜⊛Ⓐ⊙⊙Ⓟ

Royal Oak House, 54 Prince Street, Bristol BS1 4QH
Tel: 0117 904 2208

Opening times: Monday-Friday 7am-6.30pm, Saturday 8am-4pm and Sunday 9am-4pm
Veggie rating: 30% Vegetarian; 10% Vegan
Music/vibe: World
Average cost: Starters £2.95/Main dishes £5.00/Desserts £2.25
At Blue Pepper, the emphasis is on local, fresh and healthy foods free from hidden additives or unnecessary processing. Happy and willing to cater for special diets, including us veggies, there's sandwiches, rolls, salads and cakes to satisfy all. Tuck into Falafel, Organic Lebane, Tomato, Cucumber & Leaf Salad on Mezzaluna Bread or Smoked Tofu, Mixed Salad & Dairy-Free Mayo on Seeded Pain Baguette, both suitable for vegans.

Bordeaux Quay ⊜⊙⊗⊙⊙⊙⊙⊙⊙⊛

V-Shed, Canons Way, Bristol BS1 5UH
Tel: 0117 906 5550 www.bordeaux-quay.co.uk

Opening times: Restaurant: Monday-Saturday 12.30-2.30pm and 6.30-10.30pm. Brasserie: Monday-Saturday midday-3pm and 6-9.30pm and Sunday midday-7pm. Bar: Monday-Sunday midday-11pm. Deli: Monday-Saturday 9am-7pm and Sunday 10am-6pm

Veggie rating: 38% Vegetarian; 28% Vegan (on request)
Average cost: Brasserie: Starters £5.50/Main dishes
£7.50/Desserts £5.00. Restaurant: Starters £7.50/Main dishes
£14.50/Desserts £5.50

*Overlooking Arnolfini and the L-Shed, this new venture aims
at bringing customers the very best in local and organic food
and drink in environmentally-friendly surrounds. The former
warehouse – which has been stripped and redesigned using
as much of its existing materials as possible – houses a
restaurant on the first floor and brasserie, bar, deli and
bakery on the ground floor. The feel is natural, modern and
spacious. The daily changing menus reflect the best of
seasonal and local produce – expect to find dishes such as
Steamed Purple Sprouting Broccoli with a Poached Egg &
Hollandaise Sauce followed by Risotto of Chanterelles,
Spinach & Young Peconino and Amaretti Chocolate Torte
with Amaretto Cream.*

Charlies Juice Bar ⊙ ⊙ ⊙

> *5 Broad Quay, Bristol BS1 4DA*
> *Tel: 0117 927 7680 www.charliesjuicebars.co.uk*

Opening times: Monday-Friday 8am-5pm
Veggie rating: 100% Vegetarian & Vegan (juices – smoothies
can be made vegan on request and at no extra cost)
Average cost: £2.75

*Offering pure natural goodness in a glass. Sounds too good
to be true? Well don't knock it until you try it! If you're
feeling a bit low and in need of a pick-me-up why not try
Pineapple Head Juice, packed with immune boosting Vitamin
C or, if you'd like something more substantial, choose from a
selection of veggie rolls, wraps or soup (also vegan).*

The Falafel King

Broad Quay, Bristol BS1 4DA
Tel: 07855 715676

A familiar and friendly sight opposite The Watershed, nowhere delivers the goods – from its blue kiosk on the waterfront day and night – like The Falafel King. Great value for money, for just a few quid you get a large pitta stuffed with falafel, hummus & salad with a selection of sauces that just hits the spot.

The King William III Ale House ⓥ ⓞ ⓜ ⬤ ◉

20 King Street, Bristol BS1 4EF
Tel: 0117 926 8672

Opening times: Monday-Sunday midday-11pm (food served: midday-8pm)
Veggie rating: 20% Vegetarian (vegan on request)
Average cost: Starters £3.50/Main dishes £4.95

Now The King William is my kind of pub, and I'm not a big fan generally. As well as a friendly welcome, you'll find a real coal fire, cosy booths, veggie grub and vegan booze on offer, namely of the Samuel Smith variety. So thumbs, and bottoms, up!

Las Iguanas ⓞ ⓢ ⓞ ⓞ ◉

Unit A, South Building, Anchor Square, Bristol BS1 5UH
Tel: 0117 927 6233 www.iguanas.co.uk

Opening times: Monday-Thursday midday-11pm, Friday-Saturday midday-midnight and Sunday midday-10.30pm
Veggie rating: 35% Vegetarian (vegan on request)
Music/vibe: Latin American
Average cost: Starters £5.50/Main dishes £8.00/Desserts £4.00

If you need a little sunshine in your life, head for Las Iguanas and let the vibrance wash over you. Bringing a full-on Latin experience to Bristol, expect to find a heady mix of authentic dishes, mouth-watering cocktails (and non-alcoholic fruity coolers) and toe-tapping music. With an impressive capacity, including a large outdoor seating area – from contemporary sofas, to bar stools and regular tables and chairs – this is a great place to bring a crowd. Inside you'll find a cool Mediterranean vibe with paved flooring, wicker seating and wooden partitions. Lunchtime options include Chilaquiles (tortilla chips with chestnut mushrooms in a creamy smoked chilli sauce) and Grilled Aubergine Salad and evening options include Nachos, Roast Vegetables & Mixed Bean Enchilada followed by Aztec Chocolate Fudge Cake. There's also a separate children's menu where young ones can devour a main dish, dessert and endless drink for just £4.50. Also in Clifton and Bath (see pages 59 and 133).

The Olive Shed (Mediterranean)

Princes Wharf, Bristol BS1 4RN
Tel: 0117 929 1960 www.therealolivecompany.co.uk

Opening times: Tuesday-Saturday 10am-10pm and Sunday 10am-4pm

Veggie rating: 50% Vegetarian; 25% Vegan

Music/vibe: Background

Average cost: Starters £5.00/Main dishes £9.00/Desserts £4.00

Across the water from Millennium Square and just along from the L-Shed, The Olive Shed is a popular place to come and it's not difficult to see why. It has a fantastic Mediterranean feel to it and is very relaxed and welcoming. You can dine al fresco overlooking the river else head upstairs to the main dining area. Choose from dishes such as

Beetroot & Orange Salad and Pithvier of Spiced Autumn Vegetables. As well as running the restaurant, The Real Olive Company also supplies quality Mediterranean foods to restaurants, cafés and delis across the South West and sells delicacies such as grilled vegetables, stuffed olives, peppers, vinegars and cheeses from its stalls in St Nicholas Market, Clifton Down Shopping Centre and Thornbury High Street.

The Watershed Café/Bar ⊖⊗⦿⦾⊝⦿⦿⦿

1 Canons Walk, Harbourside, Bristol BS1 5TX
Tel: 0117 927 5101 www.watershed.co.uk

Opening times: Monday 11am-11pm, Tuesday-Thursday 9.30am-11pm, Friday 9.30am-midnight, Saturday 10am-midnight and Sunday 10am-10.30pm. Food served: Monday-Saturday midday-9pm and Sunday midday-7pm

Veggie rating: 40% Vegetarian; 5% Vegan

Music/vibe: Varied

Average cost: Main dishes £7.95/Jacket potatoes £4.00-£4.50/Light bites £4.00-£5.00

Part of The Watershed Media Centre, the first of its kind in Britain, which has three cinemas running a programme of films – many of which you wouldn't be able to catch at Odeon and the like – as well as workshops. From the light and airy café/bar, which has a quieter area if you're struggling to hear yourself amongst the chatter on a busy night, you can enjoy views of the harbour. The menu is made up of main dishes, which are changed every two weeks, such as Tagliatelle in White Wine & Cream Sauce with Spinach & Roasted Pine Nuts as well as soups, salads, jackets and cakes. Fair-trade and organic drinks are available, as are independent beers and wines.

City centre: Colston Street
Places to eat

Budokan (Pan-Asian) 🍴 🌚 🍥 🍱 💫 💨 ♿

31 Colston Street, Bristol BS1 5AP
Tel: 0117 914 1488 www.budokan.co.uk

Opening times: Monday-Saturday midday-2.30pm and
5.30-11pm
Veggie rating: 50% Vegetarian; 25% Vegan
Music/vibe: Ambient
Average cost: Starters £3.95/Main dishes £6.95

*Budokan's menu – served in simple, stylish surrounds with
customers eating from long communal tables – is influenced
by Japan, Thailand, Malaysia, Indonesia and Singapore and
uses original Asian recipes and authentic ingredients. And
good news for us, most of it can be adapted for vegetarians
and vegans – even the sushi – so you'll be more than spoilt for
choice. Early diners can take advantage of the 'Rapid Refuel' –
a choice of sushi, sides, rice and noodles for just £6.50 and for
the under 12s there's Baby Budokan dishes available at £3.50.
Also in Whiteladies Road, Clifton (see page 57).*

Kathmandu (Nepalese) 🍴 🍥 🍱 💫 💨

Colston Tower, Colston Street, Bristol BS1 4XE
Tel: 0117 929 4455 www.kathmandu-curry.com

Opening hours: Monday-Sunday 6-11pm
Veggie rating: 50% Vegetarian; 25% Vegan
Music/vibe: Contemporary, elegant
Average cost: Starters £3.95/Main dishes from £5.95

Beautiful family-run restaurant that has received rave reviews

*from several of the Viva! staff. It's very stylish with elegant
black décor and is quite large so a perfect choice for special
occasions. There's a large veggie menu, and the chefs readily
adapt it all to vegan without prior notice – in fact they've
been "catering for vegans for 30 years". The food is
exceptional – similar to Indian but with coconut and fruit
twists. Try the curries with lots of vegetable side dishes and
you're guaranteed a fabulous feast. Choose from Vegetable
Supreme (with herbs, coconut cream, pineapple and banana),
Garlic Vegetables and Vegetable Korma (vegan version made
with coconut cream). Thoroughly recommended.*

Zerodegrees (Microbrewery) ○ ⊗ ⦿ ◑ ⊘ ⊘ ⊙ ⊛

53 Colston Street, Bristol BS1 5BA
Tel: 0117 925 2706 www.zerodegrees.co.uk
Opening times: Monday-Saturday midday-midnight and
Sunday midday-11.30pm
Veggie rating: 20% Vegetarian (vegan on request)
Music/vibe: Chilled, jazz, funky, R&B
Average cost: Starters £4.75/Main dishes £8.00/Desserts £4.00
*This popular microbrewery is a great place to come for a
drink or to eat, particularly with a gang of friends but equally
a loved one. The contemporary, industrial setting – where
you can literally see and smell the on-site brewery around
you – holds a huge 250-seat restaurant and a large trendy
and neon-lit bar. Many of the award-winning beers are vegan
as well as unpasteurised, free of additives and colours and as
a result healthier and fresher than the mass-produced variety.
And food-wise there are some lovely pizzas, salads and pasta
dishes to choose from – my favourite's the Wood-Roasted
Vegetables Pizza. An enjoyable and unusual experience.*

Clifton: Clifton Village
Places to eat

Bauhinia (Pan-Asian) ⬤ ◑ 🉐 🆂🅳 ⬤ 🆃🅰 🅾 ⬤

5A Boyces Avenue, Clifton, Bristol BS8 4AA
Tel: 0117 973 3138 www.bauhinia-bar.co.uk

Opening times: Monday-Thursday 5-11pm, Friday-Saturday midday-midnight and Sunday midday-10pm

Veggie rating: 39% Vegetarian; 33% Vegan

Music/vibe: Dance

Average cost: Starters £4.00/Main dishes £6.50/Desserts £3.90

If your watch words for eating out are minimalist, modern and stylish then Bauhinia will be right up your street! This is a striking pan-Asian eatery over two floors with a combination of monochrome as well as cream, mint and chocolate décor which works very well. There's some unusual and colourful original artwork throughout the restaurant, and a lovely bar area downstairs with sink-into-sofas. Staff are friendly and helpful and will make you feel welcome whether you're there for a few drinks or a slap-up meal. To spot the full range of veggie options on their menu, just look for the 'V' symbol as there are several dishes containing meat for which veggie alternatives are available such as Pad Thai or Green Curry. And, if you're an early bird, you can get a great deal – a 2-course meal for just £6.90 if ordering before 7pm.

Brunel Raj (Indian) ❶ ◎ ⑫ ◉ ◉ ⊕ ♿

6-7 Waterloo Street, Clifton Village, Bristol BS8 4BT
Tel: 0117 973 2641

Opening times: Sunday-Thursday midday-2pm and
6-11.30pm and Friday-Saturday 6pm-midnight

Veggie rating: 30% Vegetarian; 20% Vegan

Music/vibe: Bengalese

Average cost: Starters £3.50/Main dishes £6.50

*A smart and quite traditional restaurant which has a
mirrored wall featuring the Clifton Suspension Bridge as well
as a panelled ceiling and framed pictures of Bristol scenes
throughout. The Brunel Raj is air conditioned so, however
hot the dish, you can keep your cool. With a wide selection
of curries available including a Vegetarian Thali and
Vegetable Kerala (packed with herbs and spices including
coriander, cumin seed, cinnamon, ginger cardamom and
fennel) there's already a good choice but you can also have
any of the 12+ side dishes as a main course too. 20% off
take-aways.*

**Don't forget to mention the Vegetarian &
Vegan Guide to Bristol & Bath when making an
enquiry or booking!**

Coffee #1 ⊖🐾🚫⊖◎🄟

31 Princess Victoria Street, Clifton, Bristol BS8 4BX
Tel: 0117 923 8021

Opening times: Monday-Saturday 8am-6pm and
Sunday 9am-6pm

Average cost: Coffees £1.70-£2.20/Smoothies £2.40-£3.00

*Great little place that offers the full range of coffees as
well as smoothies. Soya milk available. Also on Gloucester
Road, Bristol (see page 70).*

Gert Lush (Sandwich Shop) ⊘⊖◉🄟🄟🐾♿

9A Regent Street, Clifton BS8 4HW
Tel: 0117 973 1003

Opening times: Monday-Friday 7am-3pm

Veggie rating: 50% Vegetarian; 15% Vegan

Average cost: £2.00-£4.00

*A really good range of vegetarian and vegan options,
including a selection from Bristol-based vegan company
Aromafoods (see page 108). Gert Lush can deliver their
lovely veggie eats direct to your office as part of their
sandwich rounds or business lunches or you can pop in and
see what takes your fancy.*

Joy Raj (Indian) ❶🄟🄟🄟◎🐾🐾☎

31 Regent Street, Clifton, Bristol BS8 4HR
Tel: 0117 973 8101

Opening times: Sunday-Thursday 5.30-11.30pm and Friday-
Saturday 5.30pm-midnight

Veggie rating: 50% Vegetarian; 25% Vegan

Music/vibe: Indian instrumental

Average cost: Starters £2.90/Main dishes £5.50

Don't be fooled by Joy Raj's frontage – once inside and

headed downstairs you'll find a lovely restaurant with deep burgundy seating, crisp white linen and subtle Taj Mahal shapes on its ceiling. Using fresh ingredients and authentic Indian recipes, it boasts food fit for a king. There's certainly an excellent choice, with veggie versions of all the curries from a mild Korma right up to a blow-your-head-off Vindaloo. And there's also a good range of side dishes – all of which are veggie. If eating in the comfort of your own home, you can take advantage of a 20% disount on take-aways.

The Muset Restaurant (Modern European)
🍷 🆂🅳 🆆 🄽 🄾 🌀 🌀 🌀

16 Clifton Road, Clifton, Bristol BS8 1AF
Tel: 0117 973 2920 www.muset.co.uk

Opening times: Monday-Friday 6-10.15pm, Saturday-Sunday midday-2.15pm and 6-10.15pm
Veggie rating: 22% Vegetarian (vegan on request)
Music/vibe: Relaxed and jazzy
Average cost: Starters £4.50/Main dishes £13.00/Desserts £4.25

Light and relaxed restaurant blending new with old – contemporary design featuring unique artwork by local artists coupled with original and exposed stone and brick walls – making for an enjoyable dining experience. The Muset are happy to cater for special diets so vegans and those on a gluten-free diet will be looked after – just let them know in advance if possible and they'll cook you up a treat. There's a good veggie selection on offer anyway with lunch options including Somerset Brie & Vegetable Tart and Date & Walnut Pudding and evening options including Goat's Cheese Mushrooms followed by Spinach & Feta Filo Parcel and Pear & Almond Tart.

Pearl of Sri Lanka ☻◑◎◑◎☺

3A Regent Street, Clifton, Bristol BS8 4HW
Tel: 0117 973 8316 www.pearlofsrilanka.com

Opening times: Tuesday-Sunday 5.30-11.30pm

Veggie rating: 50% Vegetarian (vegan on request)

Music/vibe: Sri Lankan

Average cost: Starters from £2.95/Main dishes from £7.95/Desserts from £3.50

Simply and tastefully decorated, the Pearl of Sri Lanka provides traditional and delicious food in intimate surrounds. Dining is split over three levels and décor is understated, featuring a series of wallcarvings, white clothed tables and wooden chairs. The menu features some great veggie options such as Pumpkin Soup followed by Masala Thossai Special (pancake stuffed with masala potatoes served with lentils and coconut sambol) and then Mango Sorbet.

Pizza Provencale

29 Regent Street, Clifton, Bristol BS8 4HR
Tel: 0117 974 1175 www.pizzaprovencale.co.uk

Opening times: Friday-Saturday midday-midnight and Sunday-Thursday midday-11pm (lunch Monday-Friday midday-4pm)

Veggie rating: 24% Vegetarian (vegan on request)

Average cost: Starters £3.95/Main dishes £8.80

Don't make the mistake of thinking this is just another fast food chain. Pizza Provencale – or Pizza Prov as it's fondly known – provides customers with a candlelit and cosy setting and a menu that's both tasty and affordable. Local produce is used where possible and the dough for their pizzas is freshly baked each and every day. You can bring out the inventor in you and create your own pizza, or opt for one of their pasta dishes.

The Walrus & Carpenter Restaurant (English)
○○☾❶⑤⑩◐◯◑◐◐◍♿

1 Regent Street, Clifton, Bristol BS8 4HW
Tel: 0117 974 3793

Opening times: Monday-Friday midday-2.30pm, Saturday
midday-10.30pm and Sunday midday-9.30pm
Veggie rating: 50% Vegetarian; 10% Vegan
Average cost: Starters £4.00-£5.00/Main dishes £8.00-
£12.00/Desserts £4.00-£5.00

*Family-run restaurant, with second establishment in Bath (see
page 144), that's also family friendly too, with high chairs
provided for the little ones. With split level dining, the style of
The Walrus & Carpenter is bistro, with blue and white large
check tablecloths and curtains, round tables, terracotta floor
tiles and raspberry walls. It actually looks nicer than it sounds!
All meals are homemade using small local suppliers and organic
or locally sourced produce. There's a separate vegetarian menu
available, with dishes such as Spinach Lasagne, Nut Loaf with
Mushroom & Watercress Sauce or Mushroom Moussaka for
vegetarians and Nut Loaf with Tomato & Basil Sauce for vegans.
Drinks include a selection of wines and cocktails, which include
a Vegan Screwdriver!*

Zizi ○❶◐◐◐◍♿

29-33 Princess Victoria Street, Clifton, Bristol BS8 4BX
Tel: 0117 317 9842 www.zizzi.co.uk

Opening times: Monday-Sunday midday-11pm
Veggie rating: 30% Vegetarian (vegan on request)
Music/vibe: Modern, contemporary, pop
Average cost: Starters £3.85/Main dishes £7.75

*With its cream walls and wooden tables and chairs, the feel
of Zizzi is neutral and cool. There's a striking display, and*

what I can only describe as a large chopped wood feature, at the far end of the restaurant above the wood-burning oven (where all the pizzas are cooked) to which your eyes are immediately drawn to as you enter. On the menu is a good selection of veggie dishes from pizzas and pastas to calzone to salads. Also in Triangle South, Clifton (see page 56).

Shops

Chandos Deli
6 Princess Victoria Street, Clifton, Bristol BS8 4BP
Tel: 0117 974 3275 www.chandosdeli.com
Opening times: Monday-Tuesday 9am-5pm, Wednesday-Friday 9am-7pm, Saturday 9am-5.30pm and Sunday 10am-4pm
Their busiest shop, like other Chandos Delis this one is filled to the rafters with goodies and all the usual yummy deli delights including roasted artichokes and peppers, olives and sun-dried tomatoes as well as a good selection of take-away food such as salads, sandwiches and ciabatta baguettes, with vegan options. They do coffee too and although soya milk is sadly not available for drinks, staff have said they're happy to use if you bring your own!

Stoneground Healthfoods (Health Foods & Take-Away)
5A The Mall, Clifton, Bristol BS8 4DP
Tel: 0117 974 1260
Opening times: Monday-Friday 9am-5pm and Saturday 9am-3pm
There's a lot packed into the space here with the shop selling a varied range of health foods as well as household products and toiletries. And the take-away selection is very

good, including sandwiches, salads, Indian snacks, fresh
juices and soup, which is always vegan. Smoothies can be
made with soya yoghurt and drinks with soya milk too.

Clifton: Park Street
Places to eat

Beijing Bistro (Noodle Bar) 🌓🍜🅣🅐❤✅❤♿
72 Park Street, Bristol BS1 5JX
Tel: 0117 373 2708 www.beijingbistro.co.uk
Opening times: Sunday-Thursday midday-11pm and Friday-
Saturday midday-midnight
Veggie rating: 30% Vegetarian; 10% Vegan
Music/vibe: Modern, pop
Average cost: Side dishes £2.60-£3.40/Main dishes £5.50-£6.50
*Light and modern, the Beijing Bistro – Bristol's first oriental
noodle bar – has created a bright and fresh environment for
diners. With clean and uncluttered furnishings
complemented by framed Chinese writings and ornamental
dragons, the Bistro has small tables and chairs perfect for
couples and small groups and a large bar area. On a warm
day, the frontage fully opens so if sitting near the entrance
you can keep abreast of the hustle and bustle of Park Street.
Menu options include Vegetables & Tofu Udon Wok-Fried
Noodles or Vegetarian Satay (noodles in stock soup).*

Boston Tea Party ⬤⬤⬤⬤⬤⬤⬤⬤⬤⬤⬤⬤

75 Park Street, Bristol BS1 5PF

Tel: 0117 929 8601 www.bostonteaparty.co.uk

Opening times: Monday-Saturday 7am-8pm and Sunday 9am-8pm

Veggie rating: 50% Vegetarian (vegan on request)

Average cost: Eat-in: Sandwiches £2.75-£3.75/Main dishes £5.95-£6.95

A lovely place to come for a coffee or a spot of lunch, the Boston Tea Party has plenty of seating upstairs – including sofas and window seats overlooking Park Street – and a lovely tiered garden. Local and organic suppliers are supported where possible and 100% fairly traded coffee is used. Vegetarian and vegan options are clearly marked and they do a great range of sandwiches and wraps to eat in or take-away. Also in Bath (see page 125).

The Folk House Café & Bar ⬤⬤⬤⬤⬤⬤⬤⬤⬤

40A Park Street, Bristol BS1 5JG

Tel: 0117 908 5035 www.bristolfolkhouse.co.uk

Opening times: Monday-Thursday 9am-9pm and Friday-Saturday 9am-4pm

Veggie rating: 50% Vegetarian; 15% Vegan

Music/vibe: Folk, jazz, blues, acoustic

Average cost: Main dishes £5.50

The Folk House runs courses on everything from languages to pottery and writing to fitness/exercise. They also hold live acoustic music events most weekends as well as art exhibitions. The café is a bright and breezy no-nonsense affair, with scream-out-loud tablecloths and orange walls and a fabulous courtyard garden out front that will make you feel like you're a world away from it all. The Cooking

*Company, who run the café, cook healthy and tasty food
from scratch using organic and local ingredients. Ever-
changing, their daily menu offers at least one vegan and
three vegetarian dishes. Options include Butternut Squash &
Potato Gratin or Fiorentina Pizza with Spinach & Pine Nuts,
both served with Salad, followed by Tipsy Apricot Muffins.*

Oppo3 Music Coffee House ●○◐●◉◍●●●◐●

*72 Park Street (entrance Park Street Avenue), Clifton,
Bristol BS1 5JX
Tel: 0117 929 1166 www.oppoharmonicfusion.co.uk*
Opening times: Monday-Wednesday and Friday-Saturday
8am-6pm, Thursday 8am-10pm and Sunday 9am-5pm
Veggie rating: 40% Vegetarian; 20% Vegan
Music/vibe: Live music every Saturday at 1pm
Average cost: Main dishes £4.95/Desserts £1.20
*With its main entrance just off Park Street, Oppo3 is a music
retail area specialising in electronic/ambient music which also
just so happens to have a coffee house offering breakfasts,
sandwiches and light bites. Stop in and take a breather from
the steep climb to Queens Road.*

Shaken Stephens (Milkshake & Smoothie Bar) ●⑤●⑩

*88 Park Street, Clifton, Bristol BS2 5LA
Tel: 0117 316 9269 www.shakenstephens.co.uk*
Opening times: Monday-Friday 8am-6.30pm, Saturday 10am-
6.30pm and Sunday midday-6pm
Veggie rating: 89% Vegetarian; 35% Vegan
Average cost: £2.40/£3.20
*Independent milkshake and smoothie bar located at the top
of Park Street providing a great range of smoothies/juices as
well as jackets, soups and other snacks too. Milkshakes can be*

*made with soya milk and ice cream for 90p extra. There's a
10% student discount on offer and, a little oddly, also a 15%
discount if you wear one of their t-shirts/caps into the bar.*

Yum Yum Thai (Thai Restaurant)

○ ⚫ ⚪ ⚪ ⚪ ⚪ ⚪ ⚪ ⚪ ⚪ ⚪ ⚪

*50 Park Street, Clifton, Bristol BS1 5JN
Tel: 0117 929 0987*

Opening times: Monday-Saturday midday-2.30pm and 6-
11pm and Sunday 6-11pm
Veggie rating: 75% Vegetarian (vegan on request)
Music/vibe: Thai/jazz
Average cost: Main dishes £8.95
*Yum Yum Thai has a minimalist and modern décor with
mirrored walls and wooden furnishings. The look is finished
off with potted palms and wall-mounted Thai statuettes.
From these light and relaxed surroundings, Yum Yum Thai
serve up an excellent choice for veggies, with dishes including
their (and everyone's!) firm favourite – Vegetable Green
Curry & Rice. They're also happy to cater for vegan and other
special dietary requests. Also in Bath (see page 146).*

Shops

Culpeper & Napiers Clinic

*90 Park Street, Clifton, Bristol BS1 5LA
Tel: 0117 945 0698 www.napiers.net*

Opening times: Monday-Saturday 9.30am-6pm
*Selling a wide range of natural products including Napiers
own herbal medicines, supplements, aromatherapy oils,
flower and homoeopathic remedies and skincare, there is*

also a natural health clinic on-site providing a range of
therapies. Also in Bath (see page 148) and available online.

Also in Bath (see page 148)

Clifton: Queens Road
Places to eat

Fresh & Wild Café

85 Queens Road, Clifton, Bristol BS8 1QS
Tel: 0117 910 5930 www.freshandwild.com

Opening times: Monday-Friday 8am-8pm, Saturday 9am-7pm
and Sunday 11am-4pm

Hugely popular, the Fresh & Wild café is large, light and open with
a fantastic selection of healthy, fresh and wholesome food, much
of which is vegetarian and vegan. There are self-serve salad and
soup bars, deli and hot food counters and a eye-watering cake
display to choose from. There's also a great take-away section with
a lovely range of vegan desserts, salad pots, sandwiches and wraps.
For liquid refreshment, take your pick from coffees (try the vanilla
soya latte!), hot chocolate, teas (regular or herbal), fresh juices and
smoothies. Well worth checking out.

**Don't forget to mention the Vegetarian &
Vegan Guide to Bristol & Bath when making an
enquiry or booking!**

Le Snack ⊖ ◯ ⊗ ⚓ ⊜ ⊘ ⓑ

98 Queens Road, Clifton, Bristol BS8 1NF
Tel: 0117 974 2704

Opening times: Monday-Friday 8am-3pm
Veggie rating: 35% Vegetarian; 5% Vegan
Music/vibe: Radio 1
Average cost: Sandwiches/Paninis/Salads/Soups £2.50

Snack bar on small stretch of shops opposite Sands (see opposite). Unfortunately there are no vegan options (other than soya milk) but plenty for veggies.

Rajmoni ◑ ⓐ ◎ ⊘ ⊜

88A Queens Road, Clifton, Bristol BS8 1SA
Tel: 0117 974 1700 www.rajmoni.co.uk

Opening times: Monday-Sunday 6-11.30pm
Veggie rating: 25% Vegetarian; 10% Vegan
Music/vibe: Indian
Average cost: Starters from £2.50/Main dishes from £4.75

Now it may look a little like a scout hut from the outside, and in no way worthy of its 'Crème de la Crème' strapline but appearances can be deceiving. Inside Rajmoni is a lovely little restaurant with an open framed wooden roof, wooden shutters on its windows and formal furnishings, creating an intimate venue, perfect for a romantic night out. The owners have more than 40 years in catering and offer a wide selection of traditional and modern dishes on their menu. Dishes include Vegetable Roll (spicy vegetables and salad rolled up in a brown wheat chapatti bread) followed by Vegetable Korma (cooked with coconut) or Chana Sagwala (chickpeas and spinach). 20% discount for take-aways.

Sands (Lebanese Bar & Restaurant) 🍴🌙🅰️🟢🟢

95 Queens Road, Clifton, Bristol BS8 1LW
Tel: 0117 973 9734 www.sandsrestaurant.co.uk

Opening times: Monday-Sunday midday-2.30pm and 6-11pm
Veggie rating: 65% Vegetarian; 60% Vegan
Music/vibe: Middle Eastern
Average cost: Main dishes £9.00/Set menu £15.95

Offering something a little different, Sands has an interior that makes you feel like you're in a cavern (in a cosy rather than weird claustrophic way as it's actually deceptively spacious!) and large garden that can seat up to 100 in the summer. There's a great choice of cold and hot mezze. Dip into, for example, the exotic sounding (and not a spelling mistake!) Moussaa'at Batinjan – that's baked aubergine with chickpeas, tomatoes and spices – or sink your teeth into the Fatayer Sebanikh – pastry filled with spinach, onions, pine kernels & lemon juice. There's a 10% discount for take-aways.

Shops

Fresh & Wild
85 Queens Road, Clifton, Bristol BS8 1QS
Tel: 0117 910 5930 www.freshandwild.com
Opening times: Monday-Friday 8am-9pm, Saturday 9am-8pm
and Sunday 11am-5pm
*You won't find any artificial colours, hydrogenated fats,
flavourings, sweeteners or preservatives in this organic
supermarket, just row upon row of fresh fruit and
vegetables, breads and cakes, wines and beers, health foods,
green household products, body and skincare, baby
products, natural medicines... the list goes on and on!
Unfortunately it's not 100% veggie but a lot of it is, and
vegan too. A particular favourite are the range of fresh,
chilled desserts which include Tofu Cheesecake. Divine! And
there's a great, and very popular, café on-site too, rustling
up tasty, value-for-money organic grub (see page 51).*

Papa Costa (Deli & Café)
67 Queens Road, Clifton, Bristol BS8 1QL
Tel: 0117 929 1600
Opening times: Monday-Saturday 7am-6pm and Sunday
10am-4.30pm
*Deceptively large and tardis-like, despite its small shop front,
which stretches right back to a friendly café at the rear.
There's a good choice of veggie breakfast, paninis and
sandwiches. And they also offer a catering service, perfect
for parties.*

Clifton: The Triangle
Places to eat

Krishna's Inn (South Indian) 🍴 ⭕ 🅐 🔄 🔄

   4 Byron Place, Triangle South, Clifton, Bristol BS8 1JT
   Tel: 0117 927 6864

Opening times: Sunday-Thursday midday-3pm and 6-11pm
and Friday-Saturday midday-3pm and 6pm-midnight

Veggie rating: 60% Vegetarian; 50% Vegan

Music/vibe: Indian classical and instrumental

Average cost: Side dishes £3.95 (two for £5.00)/Main
dishes £8.00

There are lots of good Indian restaurants but few offering
authentic South Indian cuisine, such as Krishna's, so it's a real
find. A firm favourite which you won't find on other Indian
menus is the Masala Dosa – a crispy pancake made of rice
and lentils filled with potato masala – delicious! If you
become a fan (and you will) make sure you visit Monday
lunchtime/evening when Krishna's have their Dosa Festival
featuring 36 varieties! Other tasty morsels include Spinach
Vada (crunchy doughnuts or chana dal, green chillies, onion,
ginger & fresh spinach) and Erussery (pumpkin with black
eye beans & fried coconut). Sadly the décor doesn't match
the menu, with the interior conveying more of a basic café
feel rather than the South Indian sanctuary you may expect
but don't let that deter you as the food is well worth it.

Magic Roll ⬤⬤⬤🅣⬤⬤

3 Queens Row, Triangle South, Clifton, Bristol BS8 1EZ
Tel: 0117 922 1435

Opening times: Monday-Wednesday 8.30am-5pm, Thursday-Friday 8.30am-3pm and Saturday midday-3am
Veggie rating: 50% Vegetarian; 40% Vegan
Average cost: £3.25-£4.25

With a fresh and changing menu, the Magic Roll offers breakfasts, pizzas, wraps, baguettes, salads and rolls with plenty of choice for vegetarians and vegans alike. They're keen to get their customers involved so if you can think up a delicious and new filling, they'll trial it and if it's a hit, keep it on the menu. 10% discount for students.

Zizzi ⬤⬤⬤⬤⬤

7-8 Triangle South, Clifton, Bristol BS8 1EY
Tel: 0117 929 8700 www.zizzi.co.uk

Opening times: Monday-Thursday and Sunday midday-11pm and Friday-Saturday midday-11.30pm
Veggie rating: 30% Vegetarian (vegan on request)
Music/vibe: Modern, contemporary and pop
Average cost: Starters £3.85/Main dishes £7.75

Zizzi has a rich and warm décor, with burnt orange walls, cosy sofas and wooden furniture. On the menu are tasty pizzas, pastas, calzone and salads with options including Tomato Pesto Bread and Fusilli alla Genovese (roasted peppers, grilled aubergines & mushrooms in pesto sauce with crème fraiche). Also in Princess Victoria Street, Clifton (see page 45).

Clifton: Whiteladies Road
Places to eat

Bangkok House (Thai) ❶ ⑤ⓓ Ⓞ Ⓣⓐ ❸

70 Whiteladies Road, Clifton, Bristol BS8 2QA
Tel: 0117 973 0409 www.bangkokhousebristol.co.uk
Opening times: Monday-Saturday midday-3pm and 6-11pm
Veggie rating: 20% Vegetarian; 5% Vegan
Music/vibe: Thai
Average cost: Starters £3.25/Main dishes £5.75
Working to create an authentic dining experience, Bangkok House features ornately carved tables and chairs as well as a wooden framework built into its ceiling to give the diners the impression of being inside a timber roofed building. Sounds a little odd but it works! Serving up Thai food to suit all strengths of palate – from mild and subtle to hot and fiery! – to get the best experience it's suggested that a selection of dishes is ordered which you can share. Veggie dishes are listed separately and include such treats as Vegetable Tempura or Tao Hoo Tod (deep fried beancurd served with spicy peanut sauce). Yum.

Budokan (Pan-Asian) ❶ ⑭ Ⓞ Ⓣⓐ ❸ ❸ ♿

Clifton Down, Whiteladies Road, Bristol BS8 2PH
Tel: 0117 949 3030 www.budokan.co.uk
Opening times: Monday-Saturday midday-2.30pm and 5.30-11pm
Veggie rating: 50% Vegetarian; 25% Vegan
Music/vibe: Ambient
Average cost: Starters £3.95/Main dishes £6.95
Budokan apparently aim to become the most successful chain of pan-Asian restaurants in the south-west and they're

*certainly off to a good start. The emphasis is on fresh
ingredients and presentation so prepare yourself for a meal
that's beautifully tasty! Options include Sweet Potato &
Coconut Bhaja, Vegetable Sushi or Tofu Salad & Ginger Soy
Dressing. Also in Colston Street (see page 38).*

Hullaballoos Restaurant (Modern European)

46 Whiteladies Road, Clifton, Bristol BS8 2NH
Tel: 0117 923 9212 www.hullaballoos.co.uk
Opening times: Monday-Saturday midday-2.15pm and 6-
10pm and Sunday midday-2.15pm
Veggie rating: 50% Vegetarian (vegan on request)
Music/vibe: Reggae, jazz
Average cost: Starters £4.00-£6.00/Main dishes £11.00-£17.00/
Desserts £4.00-£6.00. Lunch: 2-course £9.75/3-course £12.75
*Operating from a converted Regency House, Hullaballoos
has retained many of the building's original features.
Spanning three floors and with a capacity for 150, the
restaurant has a mix of wooden furnishings and cosy semi-
circular booths, offset by exposed stone walls and original
and colourful paintings and potted flowers and plants
which create an upmarket but relaxed environment. Menu
options include Feta Cheese, Olive Oil & Roasted Red Pepper
Salad followed by Smoked Mozzarella & Vegetable Tart for
lunch and Spicy Butter Bean & Parsnip Bake for dinner,
followed by Banoffee Pie which is – according to a regular
diner there – "soooo good"!*

La Ruca – see page 76

Las Iguanas (Latin American) ⭕🟢🟠🟡🟢
113 Whiteladies Road, Clifton, Bristol BS8 2PB
Tel: 0117 973 0730 www.iguanas.co.uk
Opening times: Monday-Thursday midday-3pm and 5-11pm,
Friday-Saturday midday-11.30pm and Sunday midday-10.30pm
Veggie rating: 43% Vegetarian (vegan on request)
Music/vibe: Latin American
Average cost: Starters £5.50/Main dishes £8.00/Desserts £2.00
*This place makes a strong impression with its funky
'chandeliers', mirrored wall sections and deep red walls. The
authentic food does too with offerings such as Sopa
Pimientos (spicy roast red pepper, orange & coriander soup
with tortilla sticks & freshly baked bread), Fajitas of
Portobello Mushrooms, Butternut Squash & Artichoke and
Pastel de Maiz (corn, almond and lemon cake). Also in
Harbourside and Bath (see pages 35 and 133).*

Mandarin Classic (Chinese) 🟠🆂🅃🅰🟡🟢🟢☎
81 Whiteladies Road, Clifton, Bristol BS8 2NT
Tel: 0117 973 5095
Opening times: Monday-Thursday midday-2.30pm and 5.30-
11.30pm, Friday-Saturday midday-2.30pm and 5.30pm-
midnight and Sunday midday-10pm
Veggie rating: 20% Vegetarian; 0% Vegan
Music/vibe: Chinese
Average cost: Starters £4.50/Main dishes £6.95
*Formal and traditional restaurant with peach/terracotta
décor and two dining areas. There's a separate vegetarian
menu from which you can take your pick from three starters
and seven main courses as well as a set menu (comprising*

two courses plus tea/coffee). *Options include Mixed Hors D'Oeuvres (pancake roll, wan ton, beancurd ball & seaweed) followed by Sizzling Beancurd in Satay Sauce. The staff are very flexible – if there's a particular ingredient you're allergic to, or just don't like, let them know and they'll leave it out for you. 10% discount for take-aways.*

Planet Pizza ⊖◓◐◉◍❸❹❺

83 Whiteladies Road, Clifton, Bristol BS8 2NT
Tel: 0117 907 7112 www.planetpizza.co.uk
Opening times: Monday-Sunday 11am-11pm
Veggie rating: 63% Vegetarian (vegan on request)
Average cost: Salads £7.95/Pizzas £10.95
Voted one of the top five best pizza restaurants in the UK (Mail on Sunday, February 2006) and serving freshly prepared and authentically sourced food cooked to order. Dishes include Crostini (ciabatta topped with sundried tomatoes, fresh tomato & basil oil) and Cous Cous Salad (Moroccan spiced with roast vegetables served warm over mixed salad leaves). Vegans can even bring their own cheese to add to pizzas and other dishes (top tip: take Redwood's super melting Cheezly). Planet Pizza also has a wide range of soft drinks and milkshakes as well as coffees, bottled beers, wines and spirits. Also on Gloucester Road, Bristol (see page 72).

Quartier Vert (European) ⊖❸❻❼◐◉❸❹

85 Whiteladies Road, Clifton, Bristol BS8 2NT
Tel: 0117 973 4482 www.quartiervert.co.uk
Opening times: Monday-Saturday 10am-10pm and Sunday 10am-6pm
Veggie rating: 25% Vegetarian (vegan on request)
Music/vibe: Jazz, folk
Average cost: Starters £5.50/Main dishes £14.00/Desserts £5.00
Quartier Vert is an acclaimed restaurant, with close connections to the local organic and slow food movement as well as serious foodies. It provides simple cooking using local and organic ingredients, a principle it extends to its bakery and cookery school where it runs courses for adults and children. The restaurant – which has a cool and

*contemporary décor with aubergine and cream walls and
wooden flooring – has three dining areas (including al
fresco) as well as a large bar area. Menu options include
Muscade Squash Ravioli & Sage Butter followed by White
Onion & Gruyere Tart with Roasted Celeriac, Chicory &
Almond Salad and Chocolate Nemesis with Crème Fraiche.*

Thai Classic ❶ⓐ◎◔◑

> *87 Whiteladies Road, Clifton, Bristol BS8 2NT*
> *Tel: 0117 973 8930*

Opening times: Monday-Sunday midday-2pm and 6-11pm
Veggie rating: 30% Vegetarian (vegan on request)
Average cost: Starters £3.50-£4.50/Main dishes £5.50-£7.50
*The seating area may be a little cramped but the polite and
efficient service more than makes up for it, as does the food
which is good value for money. There are Thai and
Malaysian vegetarian set menus at £15.00, which include
starter, soup, main course and tea/coffee, or for a lighter
meal, try one of the mains. The Pad Tua-ngok (fried
beancurd with beansprouts & spring onion in soya sauce)
sounds delicious! 10% discount for take-aways.*

Shops

Chandos Deli

> *121 Whiteladies Road, Clifton, Bristol BS2 2PL*
> *Tel: 0117 970 6565 www.chandosdeli.com*

Opening times: Monday-Saturday 9am-5pm
*The oldest of the Chandos Deli chain, this place is as busy as
it's ever been and is heaving at lunchtimes. If you can find a
seat, it's a great place to grab a coffee. You can sit at the
window and watch the world go by.*

Fopp

97 Whiteladies Road, Clifton, Bristol BS8 2NT
Tel: 0117 946 7045 www.fopp.co.uk
Opening times: Monday-Saturday 9am-6pm and Sunday
11am-6pm
Not just a music store, although it's a pretty good one at
that. Upstairs there's also a café with lots of seating and
comfy chairs and soya milk for vegans/dairy intolerant. Air
conditioned. Also in Bath (see page 149).

Holland & Barrett

21 Clifton Down Shopping Centre, Whiteladies Road,
Clifton, Bristol BS8 2NN
Tel: 0117 973 8188 www.hollandandbarrett.com
Opening times: Monday-Saturday 9am-5.30pm and Sunday
11am-5pm
Located in Whiteladies shopping arcade, this store has
everything you'd expect from this high street regular. Perfect
for stocking up on health food staples as well as nibbles to
eat on the go.

Neal's Yard Remedies

126 Whiteladies Road, Clifton, Bristol BS8 2RP
Tel: 0117 946 6035
Opening times: Shop: Monday-Saturday 9.30am-6pm and
Sunday 11am-4pm. Therapy room: Monday-Friday 9am-9pm,
Saturday 9am-6pm and Sunday 11am-4pm
Whilst the Neal's Yard shop provides a variety of natural
bodycare products and remedies, its therapy room offers a
whole host of therapies including sports massage, nutrition,
life coaching, homoeopathy, allergy testing, emotional
therapy and acupuncture.

Papadeli (Deli & Café)

84 Alma Road (off Whiteladies Road), Clifton, Bristol BS8 2DT
Tel: 0117 973 6569 www.papadeli.co.uk

Opening times: Tuesday-Saturday 9.30am-4.30pm

Lovely deli with a focus on British and European foods, and stocking a great range of organic fair-trade coffee and chocolate. Also available online. The café upstairs uses products from the deli as much as possible and is a nice place to chill, though vegan options are a bit thin on the ground.

Clifton: Other
Places to eat

The Hope & Anchor (Pub) ⬤⬤⬤⬤⬤⬤⬤⬤

38 Jacobs Wells Road, Clifton, Bristol BS8 1DR
Tel: 0117 929 2987

Opening times: Monday-Saturday midday-11.30pm and Sunday midday-11pm (food served: Monday-Saturday midday-10pm and Sunday midday-9.30pm)

Veggie rating: 40% Vegetarian; 5% Vegan

Music/vibe: Background, mellow

Average cost: Main dishes £7.00

Nice pub with secluded garden and serving up wide veggie selection – with options including Falafel served with Salad & Hummus, Chilli Sauce & Tahini in Pitta (vegan) and Fresh Herb Pancakes with Broccoli, Cashews & Stilton Cream Cheese.

Rajpoot Restaurant ❶◐⚏🅰💚💚💚🄺🖕

52 Upper Belgrave Road, Clifton, Bristol BS8 2XP
Tel: 0117 973 3515 www.rajpootrestaurant.co.uk

Opening times: Monday-Saturday 6-11pm
Veggie rating: 35% Vegetarian; 30% Vegan
Music/vibe: Indian folk
Average cost: Starters £5.80/Main dishes £10.95

Enjoy fine Indian cuisine in elegant Georgian surroundings, set close to the Downs. Dishes include the delicious sounding Goa Styled Exotic Mushroom Curry and Green Vegetable Cashew Korma. Somewhere special to dine.

Siam Harbourside (Thai) ❶◐🅐💚💚

129 Hotwell Road, Clifton, Bristol BS8 4RU
Tel: 0117 330 6476 www.siam-thai.co.uk

Opening times: Tuesday-Saturday 11.30am-2.30pm and 6-11.30pm and Sunday 11.30am-2.30pm and 6-11pm
Veggie rating: 15% Vegetarian (vegan on request)
Music/vibe: Thai
Average cost: Starters £4.95/Main dishes £6.95

Take a trip to the Orient, without having to set foot outside of Bristol, by dining out at Siam Harbourside. With traditional décor – which include some fabulously ornate wooden carved armchairs and tables – the tasty authentic Thai dishes are brought to your table by staff in traditional costume. You can also enjoy good views of the river whilst tucking into dishes such as Pag Choop Paeng Tord (mixed vegetables in crispy batter) or Tom Yam Hed (mushroom soup with herbs) followed by Gaeng Pag (vegetables cooked in red curry sauce, basil & coconut cream). 10% discount on take-away orders over £20.00.

Bedminster

also see neighbouring Southville (see page 96)

Places to eat

Al's Hot & Spicy Café Bar & Restaurant (Indian)

223 North Street, Bristol BS3 1JJ
Tel: 0117 966 9008

Opening times: Monday-Saturday 6-11pm
Veggie rating: 30% Vegetarian; 20% Vegan
Average cost: Starters £2.50/Main dishes £5.95

*It may sound a little like a fast food joint, but Al's Hot &
Spicy is a more tasteful affair with its delicate lighting,
Lawrence of Arabia style paintings and décor of sandy hues.
Tables are neatly set out with hotplates, cutlery and
delicately patterned plates. From the menu you can enjoy
veggie versions of just about every curry you can think of –
from the aromatically spiced Rogan Josh to the more exotic
Vegetable Pathia – and they do a great vegetarian meal for
two for just £22.95. 10% discount on takeaways over £25.00.*

Circles (Café & Second-hand Bookshop)

65 North Street, Bedminster, Bristol BS3 1ES
Tel: 0117 966 2622

Opening times: Monday-Tuesday and Thursday-Saturday
10am-5.30pm and Sunday 10.30-4.30pm
Veggie rating: 31% Vegetarian
Average cost: Jacket potatoes £3.00-£4.00/Main dishes
£4.00-£5.00

At Circles, there's sunshine even on the wettest, darkest of days, with its bright yellow walls and orange book shelves. It's pretty small but with a seat at its large shop-front windows, it's a great place to watch the world of Bedminster go by. Menu options include a variety of all day breakfasts, paninis, jacket potatoes and cakes with specials and mains of Vegetable & Bean Casserole and Mixed Bean Bake.

Shops

Centre for Whole Health

12 Victoria Place, Bedminster, Bristol BS3 3BP
Tel: 0117 923 1138

Opening times: Monday-Friday 9am-1pm and 2-5.30pm
Natural health centre just off the beaten track offering a range of therapies including acupuncture, Chinese herbal medicine, counselling, homoeopathy, holistic massage, osteopathy and reiki.

Health Unlimited

248 North Street, Bedminster, Bristol BS3 1JD
Tel: 0117 902 0622 www.silver-gecko.com

Opening times: Monday-Friday 9am-5.30pm and Saturday 9.30am-5.30pm
Great little shop selling a fantastic selection of cards, gifts, toiletries and natural remedies. Also available online.

Masala

28 North Street, Bedminster, Bristol BS3 1HW
Tel: 0117 963 6062 www.masala.uk.com

Opening times: Monday-Tuesday and Friday 9am-6pm, Wednesday-Thursday 9am-8pm and Sunday 9am-5pm

Handy shop selling various deli items, fresh fruit and veg, take-away foods and green household products. Also has an online shop selling African and Asian gifts and furnishings.

Natural As Nature

209 North Street, Bedminster, Bristol BS3 1JH
Tel: 0845 890 1665 www.naturalasnature.co.uk
Opening times: Monday-Saturday 9am-5.30pm
Family-run business specialising in organic and fair-trade products for all the family. From organic towels to toiletries and underwear to jewellery, all products are purchased using strict ethical guidelines.

Southville Deli

262 North Street, Bedminster, Bristol BS3 1JA
Tel: 0117 966 4507 www.southvilledeli.com
Opening times: Monday-Saturday 9am-5.30pm
Wide range of deli products, organic and wholefoods, veggie wines, green household products as well as take-away coffee and snacks. There's a small seating area outside, where you can enjoy a soyaccino in the sun.

Bishopston: Gloucester Road
Places to eat

Bistro La Barrique (French) 🍷 ⊚ ⊘ ⚿ ☎

225 Gloucester Road, Bishopston, Bristol BS7 8NR
Tel: 0117 944 5500 www.bistrolabarrique.co.uk
Opening times: Monday-Sunday 11am-10pm
Veggie rating: 40% Vegetarian (vegan on request)

Music/vibe: French, modern
Average cost: Petits Plats £3.95/Side dishes £1.75-
£2.95/Starters £3.95-£5.75/Main dishes £8.75
*Run by renowned chef Michel Lemoine and aiming to inspire
and innovate, La Barrique offers French cuisine with a
Mediterranean twist. In keeping with the continental vibe
you can dine al fresco on warmer days and evenings and
watch the comings and goings of ever-popular Gloucester
Road. Its selection of French-style tapas – Petits Plats – are
perfect to share with a friend or loved one and there is a
great wine list featuring select and small independent
producers. La Barrique offers good food at an affordable
price in a warm and welcoming environment and is great for
families as children are welcomed.*

Café Delight ☺〇❶⊜⊘⊘♿

*189 Gloucester Road, Bishopston, Bristol BS7 8BG
Tel: 0117 944 1133 www.cafedelight.co.uk*
Opening times: Sunday-Wednesday 9am-6.30pm and
Thursday-Saturday 9am-10pm
Veggie rating: 25% Vegetarian; 5% Vegan
Music/vibe: Eclectic – world, funk, jazz
Average cost: Main dishes £5.00
*Fun and funky, with retro citrus walls and seating, Café
Delight is the perfect place to come the morning after the
night before although, be warned, it does get busy. You can
fill your boots with a full-on veggie breakfast, sandwich
(mine's peanut butter & banana), salad or fresh juice or no-
milk smoothie. And the griddle is guaranteed 100% veggie so
you can be sure that your breakfast won't taste of bacon!!!*

Café Neo ⊜ ◯ ⊛ ⊜

97 Gloucester Road, Bishopston, Bristol BS7 8AT
Tel: 0117 924 6506

Opening times: Monday-Sunday 8.30am-5.30pm
Veggie rating: 40% Vegetarian; 0% Vegan
Music/vibe: Blues, rock and roll
Average cost: £3.00-£5.00

Relaxed vibe with sofas by the window and yellow walls.
There's a separate veggie menu so you can go straight to
that to see what you fancy rather than have to scan the
whole menu. If you're unsure have a word with the friendly
staff. Options include breakfast, tortilla, baguettes, lasagne
and jacket potatoes as well as pastries.

Coffee #1 ⊜ ⊛ ⊜ ◯ ⓣⓐ

157 Gloucester Road, Bishopston, Bristol
Tel: 0117 942 9900

Opening times: Monday-Friday 8am-6pm, Saturday 9am-6pm
and Sunday 10am-6pm
Average cost: Coffees £1.70-£2.20/Smoothies £2.40-£3.00

Coffee #1 has nine outlets across Bristol (see page 42) and
Wales. This branch's good location and cosy vibe ensures it
continues to be a popular hang out.

Delmonico ◯ ⊛ ⓘ ◯ ⊛ ⊛ ⊛ ☎

217 Gloucester Road, Bishopston, Bristol BS7 8NN
Tel: 0117 944 5673 www.delmonico.co.uk

Opening times: Tuesday-Friday from 5pm, Saturday from
noon and Sunday noon-2.30pm
Veggie rating: 25% Vegetarian (vegan on request)
Music/vibe: Jazz, swing
Average cost: Starters £5.50/Main dishes £11.95

Stylish and intimate restaurant and café/bar providing affordable dining which can be enjoyed both inside and in the outdoor seating area. The restaurant menu – which includes influences from classic Anglo-French to contemporary with an American, Asian or Italian influence – changes regularly and is based on local produce. The wine list focuses on French classics. Sample dishes include Parmesan Pastry Tart of Blue Cheese, Leek & Mushrooms with a Spicy Tomato Sauce followed by Baked Aubergine & Spiced Tofu with Roasted Peppers and Mediterranean Bean & Tomato Salsa and to finish Rhubarb Sundae. Meanwhile the cafe/bar's emphasis is on tapas, lighter meals and antipasto dishes.

Ezo Turkish Restaurant ❶ⓘ◑◐⑥

6 The Promenade, Gloucester Road, Bishopston, Bristol BS7 8AJ
Tel: 0117 944 2005

Opening times: Monday-Sunday midday-11pm
Veggie rating: 70% Vegetarian; 50% Vegan
Music/vibe: Authentic Eastern music
Average cost: Starters £3.50/Main dishes £8.00

Ezo Turkish is authentically decorated with patchwork wallhangings, wooden flooring and mustard walls. There's a charcoal BBQ so you could get the waft of meat cooking whilst tucking into your meal. But this place is great for veggies as over half of the hot mezze and almost all of the cold mezze are veggie. Dishes include Vegetable Kebab (aubergine, peppers & tomatoes with an oriental sauce) and cold mezze of Ezme (spicy red pepper, green pepper tomato, onions & mixed herbs), Dolma or Kisir (cous cous salad with spices & herbs).

Planet Pizza ⭕🍷🍵🍲🍲♿

> *187 Gloucester Road, Bishopston, Bristol BS7 8BG*
> *Tel: 0117 944 4717 www.planetpizza.co.uk*

Opening times: Monday-Sunday 11am-11pm
Veggie rating: 65% Vegetarian (vegan on request)
Average cost: Salads £7.95/Pizzas £10.95

Planet Pizza was voted one of the top five pizza restaurants in the UK by the Mail on Sunday in 2006. As the name may suggest, all the pizzas – which are big enough to share – are named after planets and if none take your fancy, you can even create your own (and take your own vegan cheese to add too). They do some great specials including buy-one-get-one-free Sunday-Wednesday 5-7pm and a daily lunchtime offer of quarter pizza and salad for just £3.95. Also on Whiteladies Road, Clifton (see page 61).

Prince of Wales (Pub) ⭕🐾🍷🍲🍲♿

> *5 Gloucester Road, Bishopston, Bristol BS7 8AA*
> *Tel: 0117 924 5552*

Opening times: Monday-Saturday 10am-midnight and Sunday midday-midnight
Veggie rating: 35% Vegetarian; 10% Vegan
Music/vibe: Chilled/up-tempo depending on time of day
Average cost: Starters £4.50/Main dishes £6.95-£9.80

Not just the perfect place for a lunchtime or evening drink, but for veggies to eat too. The Prince of Wales offers several vegetarian specials and mains and at least one vegan special too. You can expect to see dishes such as Stuffed Roast Butternut Squash, Veggie Sausage & Mash, Veggie Breakfast, Sunday Nut Roast and Stir-fry Tofu on the menu. Cheers guys!

Sheesh Mahal Tandoori Restaurant

❶ ◎ ⒯ ⦿ ⦿ ⓖ ☎

13A Gloucester Road, Bishopston, Bristol BS7 8AA
Tel: 0117 942 2942

Opening times: Monday-Sunday midday-2pm and 6-11.30pm
Veggie rating: 25% Vegetarian; 20% Vegan
Music/vibe: Sitar
Average cost: Starters £3.60/Main dishes £5.60

Just a couple of doors up from Harvest (see page 76), Sheesh Mahal is hard to miss, on account of its colourful frontage which features blue mosaic tiling and pink curtains. It's striking! Once inside, you can slope off to a cosy booth and enjoy a tasty feast at this popular and long-established restaurant. Dishes include Vegetable Gustofa and Vegetable Moricha and you can take your pick from a range of wines, spirits and soft drinks. 20% discount for take-aways.

Simply Thai Take-Away

67 Gloucester Road, Bishopston, Bristol BS7 8AD
Tel: 0117 924 4117

Opening times: Tuesday-Sunday midday-2.30pm and 5.30-10.30pm
Veggie rating: 20% Vegetarian (vegan on request)
Average cost: Starters £2.95/Main dishes £3.95/Desserts £2.00

As the name suggests, this take-away – which has limited seating so you can eat-in too – cooks up simple, tasty Thai food. Veggie options are clearly marked and include Tofu with Ginger & Chinese Leaves although, as food is made to order, they can deal with vegan and other special dietary requests.

Spice Route (Coffee Bar & Deli) ⊝◯⊜◐◑♿

61 Gloucester Road, Bishopston, Bristol BS7 8AD
Tel: 0117 904 0040

Opening times: Monday-Saturday 8am-5pm
Veggie rating: 50% Vegetarian; 10% Vegan
Music/vibe: Mellow, jazz
Average cost: £2.50-£3.95

Attractive coffee bar and deli serving a range of tasty eats from paninis and baked potatoes to salads and smoothies. The light, relaxed décor of Spice Route is really appealing, with its archways, mirrors and terracotta walls, making it the perfect pit-stop for Gloucester Road shoppers.

Shops

Bishopston Trading Co Ltd

193 Gloucester Road, Bishopston, Bristol BS7 8BG
Tel: 0117 924 5598 www.bishopstontrading.co.uk

Opening times: Monday-Saturday 9.30am-5.30pm
One of five shops across the region selling fair-trade and organic clothing, bags, jewellery, bed linen and other products, combining English design with Indian craftmanship. Also in Bradford-on-Avon (see page 162).

Books For Amnesty

103 Gloucester Road, Bishopston, Bristol BS7 8AT
Tel: 0117 942 2969 www.booksforamnesty.org.uk

Opening times: Monday-Friday 10am-4pm and Saturday 11am-5pm
Find a bargain and support human rights organisation Amnesty International at the same time by having a root

through Books For Amnesty's shelves. There's something for everyone and maybe once you've read what you've bought you could donate it back again. Now that's recycling!

BORN

   64 Gloucester Road, Bishopston, Bristol BS7 8BH
   Tel: 0117 924 5080 www.borndirect.com
Opening times: Monday-Saturday 9.30am-5.30pm
The leading UK retail supplier of natural and organic baby products, BORN has shops in Gloucester Road and Stoke Newington, London, as well as its online shop. From nursing bras to real nappies and natural remedies to helpful books, BORN has everything you could possibly need to bring up your baby naturally, ensuring that harsh and possibly harmful products are avoided, and supporting fairly traded and organic businesses.

The Bread Store

   45 Gloucester Road, Bishopston, Bristol BS7 8AD
   Tel: 0117 942 1654
Opening times: Monday-Saturday 8am-6pm (although you'll probably catch them open much earlier!)
You know they've got to be good when you can't even get in! It's not uncommon to queue outside The Bread Store but as its current customers know it's worth it to get "the best bread in town".

Bristol Buddhist Centre

   162 Gloucester Road, Bishopston, Bristol BS7 8NT
   Tel: 0117 924 9991 www.bristol-buddhist-centre.org
Opening times: Monday-Saturday 1-4pm (shop)
Take the path to enlightenment – step into the Bristol

Buddhist Centre and you'll find classes, courses and retreats in Buddhism, Buddhist meditation and yoga as well as a shop stocked full of Buddhist, meditation, yoga and other goodies.

Harvest

11 Gloucester Road, Bishopston, Bristol BS7 8AA
Tel: 0117 942 5997 www.harvest-bristol.coop
Opening times: Monday-Saturday 9am-6pm
Though not as large as its Walcot Street store in Bath (see page 150), there's still a great 100% veggie choice, with a yummy take-away section right by the door, fresh breads and organic fruit/veg, wines, chilled and other health foods, weigh your own pulses, seeds and muesli as well as a good hair and body care range. Part of the Essential Trading Co-operative, and in business for over 30 years, this is a firm favourite.

The Healing Rooms

162 Gloucester Road, Bishopston, Bristol BS7 8NT
Tel: 0117 944 3173 www.healingroomsbristol.co.uk
Opening times: Monday-Saturday 1-4pm (reception)
Just above the Bristol Buddhist Centre, the Healing Rooms offers a wide range of therapies for physical and emotional wellbeing.

La Ruca (Health Foods, Take-Away & Café)

89 Gloucester Road, Bishopston, Bristol BS7 8AB
Tel: 0117 944 6810
Opening times: Monday-Saturday 9am-5.30pm
With its baskets of cups and other Columbian pottery pieces outside, you can't miss La Ruca. Selling a wide range of organic, fair-trade, natural and environmentally friendly products, it ticks all the boxes. And its tapas take-away is the icing on the cake. Café upstairs provides good home-cooked

fare of the South American persuasion, with vegans being able to enjoy several options, including soya milkshakes. Yay!

Osna (Complementary Therapy Centre)

234 Gloucester Road, Bishopston, Bristol BS7 8NZ
Tel: 0117 907 5884 www.osna.co.uk

Opening times: Tuesday-Saturday 10am-8pm
Offering a range of treatments – as well as courses and lectures – centring around aromatherapy, reflexology and massage to make the body more relaxed and therefore able to look after itself and heal more quickly. Cost £20.00-£35.00 for treatments. Osna also sell a range of organic products including bath bombs, soaps and essential oils. Gift vouchers available.

Scoopaway

113 Gloucester Road, Bishopston, Bristol BS7 8AT
Tel: 0117 987 2199

Opening times: Monday-Saturday 9am-5.30pm
A lot of 'weigh and save' places fell by the wayside after their hey-day but we're so glad that this health food haven lasted the course as it's a real money-saver. Get grappling with the scooper and fill your boots with pulses, nuts, seeds, cereals, dried fruits and other staples. Lovely and helpful staff too.

Cleeve
Places to eat

Coffee Shop at Cleeve Nursery & Garden Centre

Main Road, Cleeve, Bristol BS49 4PW
Tel: 01934 832134 www.cleevenursery.co.uk

Opening times: Nursery: Monday-Saturday 9am-5pm (Winter) and 9am-6pm (Summer) and Sunday/Bank Holidays 10am-5pm

Cleeve Nursery takes full advantage of its location near an active heronry by having its very own HeronCam during the nesting season (February/March). You can keep track of one nest's occupants from the shop monitor or view from the comfort of your own home via the Internet. In the café you'll find several veggie options and vegans can also tuck into either the apricot or oaty mincemeat slice. The owners are also thinking about providing soya milk so if you pop in please do ask.

Cotham
Places to eat

Blue Juice ☻ ◗ ☻ ◗ ☻ ⑯ ☻ ☻

39 Cotham Hill, Cotham, Bristol BS6 6JY
Tel: 0117 973 4800

Opening times: Monday-Friday 8am-5pm and Saturday 9am-5pm

Veggie rating: 80% Vegetarian; 50% Vegan

Music vibe: Reggae, jazz, blues

Average cost: Wraps £2.95-£3.95/Salads £2.95/Main dishes £4.50

Whatever the weather, Blue Juice is a great place to hang, but it's especially nice on a warm sunny day when you can sit round one of the big wooden tables and enjoy a freshly blended juice or smoothie and, if you're peckish, a wrap, salad or hot dish of the day. With its vibrant blue and orange frontage, this is the pick of the Cotham crop.

The Pickled Onion (Sandwich & Espresso Bar)

10 Cotham Hill, Cotham, Bristol BS6 6LF
Tel: 0117 923 8840

Opening times: Monday-Friday 8am-4pm and Saturday 9am-3pm
Veggie rating: 30% Vegetarian; 5% Vegan
Music/vibe: Radio
Average cost: £2.50
Nice little café offering a selection of sandwiches, paninis, melts and jacket potatoes, with a good choice for veggies and a few options for vegans too (you really can't go wrong with Hummus & Roasted Veg!). The décor is warm and inviting.

Shops

Amphora Aromatics

36 Cotham Hill, Cotham, Bristol BS6 6LA
Tel: 0117 904 7212 www.amphora-retail.com

Opening times: Monday & Saturday 9.30am-5pm and Tuesday-Friday 9.30am-5.30pm
More than just a shop, Amphora Aromatics is a thriving online business and wholesaler too so you can get their lovely goodies sent to you wherever you are in the UK. The

shelves are packed with lovely natural beauty products, essential oils, bodycare, plant wax candles, aromatherapy, books, natural medicines and supplements, hemp products and much more.

Earthbound (Health Foods)

   8 Abbotsford Road, Cotham, Bristol BS6 6HB
   Tel: 0117 904 2260
Opening times: Monday-Saturday 9am-6pm
The place to shop in Cotham with fresh locally sourced and organic where possible fruit and vegetables, wholefoods, groceries, speciality breads, chutney, chocolate and bodycare.

The Natural Health Clinic

   39 Cotham Hill, Cotham, Bristol BS6 6JY
   Tel: 0117 974 1199 www.thenaturalhealthclinic.com
Opening times: Monday-Friday 9am-6pm and Saturday 9.30am-2pm
Located next to Blue Juice (see page 78), the clinic has a team of more than 20 practitioners, making it Bristol's largest – as well as longest established – centre for complementary medicine. Therapies include sports massage, kinesiology, hypnosis and aromatherapy.

Don't forget to mention the Vegetarian & Vegan Guide to Bristol & Bath when making an enquiry or booking!

Easton
Places to eat

Café Maitreya (European)

⬤⬤⬤⬤⬤⬤⬤⬤⬤⬤⬤⬤⬤⬤⬤

> 89 St Mark's Road, Easton, Bristol BS5 6HY
> Tel: 0117 951 0100 www.cafemaitreya.co.uk

Opening times: Tuesday-Saturday from 6.45pm (last orders 9.45pm)
Veggie rating: 100% Vegetarian; 50% Vegan
Music/vibe: Background
Average cost: 2-course £16.50/3-course £20.25

The UK's Best Vegetarian Restaurant, as voted by the Vegetarian Society for the last two years, Café Maitreya has a lot to live up to, but continue to do so it does. This is a delightful place to eat with modern, calming décor, friendly staff and a fantastic menu of course. Always seasonal, and often organic and local, the imaginative menu changes regularly but you can expect to tuck into such treats as Provencal Artichoke & Truffle Potato Gratinee followed by Cherry, Chocolate & Almond Parfait. Leads the way.

Eastern Taste ⬤⬤⬤⬤⬤⬤⬤⬤

> 94 St Marks Road, Easton, Bristol BS5 6JH
> Tel: 0117 952 0718

Opening times: Monday-Saturday midday-2pm and 6-11pm
Veggie rating: 85% Vegetarian & Vegan
Music/vibe: Bangladeshi
Average cost: Starters £2.50/Main dishes £3.90

The blue and white check cloths and matching décor may not be quite what you'd expect but there's cheap and tasty

*fare on offer at this Bangladeshi eatery, which is popular
with the locals. Don't expect high cuisine, just good, basic,
fresh food served by lovely staff. Dishes include Aloo Chat
followed by Mushroom & Vegetable Passanda or Mixed
Vegetable Rogan. 10% discount on take-aways.*

La Casbah (Moroccan) 🂠 🌑 🆃🅰 ♻

*96 St Marks Road, Easton, Bristol BS5 6JD
Tel: 0117 939 8804 www.lacasbah.co.uk*
Opening times: Monday-Thursday 11am-3pm and 6-11pm
and Friday-Saturday 11-3pm and 6pm-midnight
Veggie rating: 40% Vegetarian (vegan on request)
Average cost: Starters £2.50/Main dishes £5.80
*This family-run business was the first of its kind in Bristol and
now, some 10 years on, has grown into an atmospheric
Moroccan restaurant. The brick colour walls are adorned
with a series of murals evoking the Moroccan lifestyle and
lanterns hang from the ceiling. The food is original and
authentic and the menu offers many veggie dishes including
Harrera (a traditional soup of celery, chickpeas, tomatoes,
coriander & mixed spices) and Vegetable Tajine.
10% discount on take-aways.*

Shops

Bristol Sweet Mart

*80 St Marks Road, Easton, Bristol BS5 6JH
Tel: 0117 951 2257 www.bristolsweetmart.co.uk*
Opening times: Monday-Saturday 9am-7pm and Sunday
11am-5pm
Most of its shop customers are probably unaware, but the

Bristol Sweet Mart is the biggest supplier of ethnic foods and spices in the south-west. More of a supermarket than sweet mart, it's a great place to do your shopping, especially if you like to cook. Choose from an extraordinary range of foods from across the world – from Polish to Caribbean, Indian to Pakistani and more – there's something to get everybody's juices going! From a wide selection of fruit and veg to a mind-boggling variety of noodles and shelves of bottled and tinned pickled veggies, it's all good quality and very reasonably priced. Just be warned: you'll come out with a lot more than you bargained for!

Henleaze
Shops

Chandos Deli

97 Henleaze Road, Henleaze, Bristol BS9 4JP
Tel: 0117 907 4391 www.chandosdeli.com

Opening times: Monday-Friday 8.45am-5pm and Saturday 8.30am-5pm

Once you set foot inside Chandos Deli you'll be greeted by a large display of baked goods, cheeses and delicious veggie items. Now you have to decide what to buy from the hundreds of products on sale, sourced both locally and from across Europe and beyond. Why not take your time and have a coffee whilst you mull it over?

Horfield: Gloucester Road
Places to eat

Cibo Ristorante ○ ◐ ◑ ◐ ◑ ◐ ◑ ◐ ◐

289 Gloucester Road, Horfield, Bristol BS7 8NY
Tel: 0117 942 9475 www.cibo.co.uk

Opening times: Deli & café bar: Monday-Thursday 10.30am-
10.30pm, Friday-Saturday 9.30am-11pm and Sunday midday-
5pm. Restaurant: Monday-Sunday midday-2.30pm and
6-10.30pm

Veggie rating: 30% Vegetarian (vegan on request)

Music/vibe: Easy listening

Average cost: Starters £5.95/Main dishes £13.95

*Family-run Italian business Cibo provides wholesale produce
to hotels, restaurants and delis and has an online store from
which you can order pastas, wines, preserves and teas. Its
restaurant is stylish and intimate offering diners a selection of
authentic Italian dishes. Menu options include Focaccia with
Rosemary, Onion, Sea Salt & Extra Virgin Olive Oil followed
by Spaghetti with Garlic, Olive Oil & Chilli or Risotto with
Fresh Vegetables & Herbs & Parmesan and to finish Ice Cream.
These can be enjoyed with a selection of Italian wines.*

Fungs (Chinese Restaurant & Take-Away) ◐ ◐ ◐ ◐

330 Gloucester Road, Horfield, Bristol BS7 8TJ
Tel: 0117 923 2020 www.fungs-chinese.co.uk

Opening times: Wednesday-Saturday midday-2pm and
Monday-Sunday 5.30-11pm

Veggie rating: 40% Vegetarian (vegan on request)

Music/vibe: Chinese

Average cost: Starters £1.30/Main dishes £4.00/Set meal for two £10.00

Simply decorated, with dark green floor tiles and beige walls, Fungs provides a good choice for veggies, with a good tofu selection and vegetarian options clearly marked. Choose from Mixed Vegetables & Tofu Soup or Vegetable Pancake Rolls and Tofu with Szechuan Kungpou Chilli Sauce & Cashew Nuts. As dishes are made to order these, and other veggie options, can easily be adapted for vegans.

The Ganges (Indian) 🍴 ⬤ 🆃🅰 ⬤ ⬤ ⬤

   368 Gloucester Road, Horfield, Bristol BS7 8TP
   Tel: 0117 924 5234

Opening times: Monday-Sunday midday-2pm and 6-11.30pm
Veggie rating: 50% Vegetarian; 45% Vegan
Music/vibe: Indian instrumental
Average cost: Starters £3.00/Main dishes £6.00-£7.00

A popular restaurant that's been in business for over 25 years and can count among its many fans, past and present, celebrities such as Keith Floyd and Shakin Stevens. Traditionally decorated with golden arched booths, The Ganges consistently serves up good Indian food from across the region and the Navratan Pulaw (nutty, fruity dish served with Dal Samba) is a firm favourite. 10% discount on take-aways.

Mad About Sarnies 🆂🅳 ⬤ ⬤ 🆃🅰

   307A Gloucester Road, Horfield, Bristol BS7 8PE
   Tel: 0117 942 5963

Opening times: Monday-Friday 8.30am-3.30pm and Saturday 9.30am-3.30pm
Veggie rating: 35% Vegetarian (vegan on request)
Average cost: £2.00

Bright and funky and perfect for food on the go. Mad About Sarnies provides lunches, buffets and picnic hampers using the best quality and freshest ingredients. Veggie sandwiches, available on a variety of breads, are clearly marked, and there's also a choice of pick 'n' mix salads, wraps and melts. There are gluten-free cakes too.

New Taj Takeaway (Tandoori) ⊜ Ⓥ Ⓐ ⦿

404 Gloucester Road, Horfield, Bristol BS7 8TR
Tel: 0117 942 1992

Opening times: Monday, Wednesday, Thursday & Sunday 5.30pm-midnight and Friday-Saturday 5.30pm-12.30am
Veggie rating: 30% Vegetarian (vegan on request)
Average cost: Starters £2.50/Main dishes £4.50/Set meal for two £13.95

If you're fighting off a cold or flu, don't reach for the drugs, drag yourself down to the New Taj instead. The canny owner has come up with a novel creation called "Flu-Indaloo" – a veggie version of which is available – which contains a cocktail of health-promoting ingredients including chillies, cloves, coriander, garlic, ginger and mustard seeds. Apparently it's not as hot as you'd think, has been given the thumbs-up taste-wise and, if nothing else, should help clear those sinuses for sure!

Shops

Bristol Natural Health Service

407 Gloucester Road, Horfield, Bristol BS7 8TS
Tel: 0117 944 4448 www.bristolnaturalhealthservice.co.uk

Opening times: Monday-Friday 10am-1pm and 2-5pm

Offers a wide range of therapies, taking into account patient's attitudes, lifestyle, vital energy and posture as well as symptoms. All are safe, non-toxic, non-addictive and have no side effects. Treatments include acupuncture, allergy testing, aromatherapy, craniosacral therapy, children's clinic, counselling and psychotherapy, homoeopathy, hypnotherapy, herbal medicine, massage, McTimoney Chiropractic, Reiki, Reflexology and Shiatsu. Free consultations are available with qualified and experienced practitioners and evening appointments are available for many treatments. The cost of therapies, for which gift vouchers are available, range from £20.00-£60.00. The centre also runs various free talks about treatments and conditions – check their website for details.

Hotwells
Places to eat

Create Café ⊕ ⊙ ⊖ ⊘ ⊕

CREATE Centre, Smeaton Road, Hotwells BS1 6XN
Tel: 0117 925 0505

Opening times: Monday-Friday 8.30am-2pm
Veggie rating: 50% Vegetarian (vegan on request)
Average cost: £2.95

The CREATE Centre is an environment centre which hosts a range of events and exhibitions, as well as being home to the purpose built Ecohome, several sustainability organisations and the Create Café. Frequented by the Centre's workers as well as visitors, the café – which has views of the river – offers fair-trade liquid refreshment and food that's fresh and local.

Montpelier
Places to eat

A-Roy/Ying Thai Oriental (Thai Oriental Restaurant & Take-Away) 🔵🔵🔵🔵🔵🔵

215 Cheltenham Road, Montpelier, Bristol BS6 5QP
Tel: 0117 924 9402

Opening times: Monday-Saturday 6-11pm and Sunday 5.30-10.30pm

Veggie rating: 25% Vegetarian (vegan on request)

Average cost: Starters £2.95/Main dishes

A-Roy has a neutral décor with sculpted wooden chairs, spot lighting and a mix of synthetic and real flower and plant displays. From its two dining areas you can enjoy freshly cooked Thai food. All dishes that can be prepared as veggie are clearly marked and any of the set dinners can be made veggie too – try the Vegetables in Batter or Tom Kha (mild coconut curry with mushrooms, lemongrass, galangal & lemon juice). Tasty.

Indian Fast Food (Restaurant & Take-Away) 🔵🔵🔵🔵🔵

203B Cheltenham Road, Montpelier, Bristol BS6 5QX
Tel: 0117 924 8062

Opening times: Sunday-Monday and Wednesday-Thursday 5.30-11.30pm and Friday-Saturday 5.30pm-midnight

Veggie rating: 20% Vegetarian (vegan on request)

Average cost: Starters £2.10/Main dishes £3.50/Thali £7.75

Great for a meal out, or at home, Indian Fast Food ticks the boxes in terms of taste, service and value-for-money. The

Vegan 999

You can count on us to fulfil all of your emergency vegan needs... from satisfying that irrepressible chocolate craving to finding the perfect cruelty-free gift and providing an inspiring read to wearing your heart on your sleeve (or mug or fridge magnet!). Just give us a ring on 0117 944 1000 (Monday-Friday, 9am-6pm), shop on our website at www.viva.org.uk or just send your name, address, order and a cheque (payable to Viva!) to the address below. Don't forget to add p&p: 50p (under £2), £1 (under £5), £2 (under £15) and £3 (under £20).

Pigs Just Wanna Have Fun Mug, £3.95
Get your work colleagues thinking with this colourful mug, with happy pig illustration and 'Pigs Just Wanna Have Fun' slogan.

Vegan, Organic Chocolate Bar with Caramel, £1.55
Worth every last penny, this delight will convince you that veganism is nowt to do with deprivation! Savour the sweet caramel as it mingles seductively with the deep, dark chocolate. Mmm.

If It's Got A Face I Don't Eat It T-shirt, £12, Mocha
This stunning design is undeniably eyecatching and as well as turning heads, will also be educating the masses. Available in:
Close-fit
a) small
b) medium
c) large and
Unisex
d) small
e) medium
f) large.

Vegan Freak, paperback, £8
Written by professors Bob and Jenna Torres, this engaging (and sometimes irreverent) book will keep both new and stalwart vegans motivated.

Fridge Magnet, 80p
Keep your kitchen a haven for the animals with this 'Meat Free Zone' fridge magnet.

Viva! 8 York Court, Wilder Street, Bristol BS2 8QH
Tel: 0117 944 1000 Email: info@viva.org.uk www.viva.org.uk

Vegetarian Meal for Two is just £11.50 (and vegan bar the yoghurt dip and naan) and a feast but if you don't fancy a blow-out why not split it and have it for dinner and then lunch the following day – bargain!

Mela Indian Take-Away 🆃🅐 ⊘

19 York Road, Montpelier, Bristol BS6 5QB
Tel: 0117 924 9272

Opening times: Monday-Thursday & Sunday 6-11pm and Friday-Saturday 6pm-midnight
Veggie rating: 50% Vegetarian; 25% Vegan
Average cost: Starters £1.50/Main dishes £3.00-£4.00
This great little take-away, located opposite One Stop Thali (see opposite), is very popular with veggies and unsurprisingly so. It cooks up a wide range of delicious vegetarian and vegan dishes and all food is freshly prepared by an experienced chef of over 25 years. Perfect for a night in.

Oh! Calcutta! (Indian) 🌶🅞🆃🅐⊘☎♿

216 Cheltenham Road, Montpelier, Bristol BS6 5QU
Tel: 0117 924 0458 www.ohcalcutta.co.uk

Opening times: Monday-Sunday 6-10.30pm
Veggie rating: 60% Vegetarian (vegan on request)
Music/vibe: Chill out
Average cost: Starters £3.00/Main dishes £8.50
Fresh and exciting Indian cuisine in a modern, relaxed and friendly environment. Dishes are given a spicy rating from 0-3. I tend to hover between 0-1 (what a softie) so you can imagine how horrified I was to see that the Oh! Phall dish is rated as a whopping 6 and is "painfully hot on both tongue and cheeks". Yikes - I hope I never order that by mistake! Dishes include Vegetable Pakora and Malaysian Curry (fresh

*tomatoes with pineapple & coconut milk). There's a
generous 20% discount on take-away orders placed 6-7pm
and 10-11pm, 10% discount at other times.*

One Stop Thali Café (Indian) ⊝ ⊙ ⭕ ◑ ◕ ⑩ ⑫ ⭕ ◔ ⊙

12 York Road, Montpelier, Bristol BS6 5QE
Tel: 0117 952 6687 www.onestopthali.co.uk
Opening times: Tuesday-Sunday 6pm-midnight
Veggie rating: 100% Vegetarian; 75% Vegan (set menu)
Music/vibe: Eclectic – live music on Sundays
Average cost: Starters £2.95/Thalis £6.95/Desserts £2.95
*Offering simply tasty food in ethnic and vibrant surrounds,
and at a great price, One Stop Thali is much loved and
always busy so make sure you book! With a capacity of 35,
this cosy eatery is perfect for enjoying an intimate night out.
There's no menu as such – instead the Punjabi chef cooks up
a series of complementary dishes to form the daily-changing
Thali menu. The resulting feast should satisfy your hunger
pangs but if not ask them for a top-up and they'll gladly
oblige – for free! On Sunday nights enjoy an eclectic mix of
live music from local performers. You can also enjoy great
Thali food to go as One Stop Thali also offer a fab eco take-
away scheme – you buy one of their insulated tiffins and you
can use over and over again. Genius!*

Plantation (Caribbean Restaurant) 🌐 🕤 🕕 🆂🅳 🐽 🔘 🅃🅰 😊 🐾

221-223 Cheltenham Road, Montpelier, Bristol BS6 5QP
Tel: 0117 907 1597 www.plantationrestaurant.biz

Opening times: Tuesday-Thursday 6-11pm, Friday-Saturday 6-11.30pm and Sunday 6-10pm

Veggie rating: 40% Vegetarian & Vegan

Music/vibe: Caribbean, reggae, African, jazz reggae

Average cost: Starters £4.25-£4.95/Main dishes £10.25-£12.00

Guaranteed 100% authentic, Plantation is a great place to come with a party – as it's large, light and open. The décor is cool Caribbean with colourful flags adorning the ceiling, white tablecloths, black furniture and wooden flooring. To complete the effect, there are even wooden shutters on the windows, though hopefully there's no chance of a hurricane heading our way! And while you tuck into your Callaloo Fritters, Jerk Tofu with Stir Fried Vegetables and plantain or rice & peas, you can admire the striking paintings created by the UK's most talented African artists. Veggie and gluten-free items are clearly marked and staff can easily advise you of vegan items too. On Fridays and Saturdays there's an all-you-can-eat buffet for £17.95, much of which is veggie. 10% discount on take-away orders.

Shops

Herberts Bakery

12 York Road, Montpelier, Bristol BS6 5QE
Tel: 0117 924 7713 www.herbertsbakery.co.uk

Opening times: 8am-4pm

Something of an institution, Herbert's have been supplying an ever-expanding array of breads to shops, restaurants and

cafés across Bristol for over 40 years now. They also have their own shop adjoining the bakery but you'll have to get there early as the loaves – and selection of cakes and savouries – fly off the shelves. Unfortunately, there's some confusion as to which products are suitable for vegans – the listings in the staff handbook are not, at the time of writing, correct – so do check carefully.

Radford Mill Farm Shop

41 Picton Street, Montpelier, Bristol BS6 5PZ
Tel: 0117 942 6644

Opening times: Monday-Friday 9am-7pm and Saturday 10am-5pm

For its size, this little shop packs a punch stocking a good variety of health foods as well as organic fruit and veg, although it is a bit of a squeeze. In the adjoining area to the shop there's also a café/juice bar.

Seven Generations (Green Goods)

10-12 Picton Street, Montpelier, Bristol BS6 5QA
Tel: 0845 223 5435 www.sevengenerations.co.uk

Opening times: Monday-Saturday 10am-6pm

If you want to be green, this is the place to be seen! Packed with all manner of recyclable, biodegradable and compostable items – as well as a great selection of books – you can shop safe in the knowledge that you're doing your bit for the planet. Boasting brands such as Bio-D, Weleda, Still Room, Natracare, Ecover, Green People, Yaoh, Urtekram, Faith In Nature, Aqua Oleum, Biofa, Osmo, Tushies, Moltex, Clearspring, Clean, Greenglass, Eco-logic plus more, you're spoilt for choice.

Wongs Acupuncture Clinic

206 Cheltenham Road, Montpelier, Bristol BS6 5QU
Tel: 0117 942 7467

Opening times: Monday-Friday 10am-6pm and Saturday 10am-4.30pm

Offering, as you would expect, acupuncture but also reflexology and massage. Treatments for these start at £25.00, with a consultation costing £10.00-£20.00 (£5.00 follow-up). There's also herbal remedies available with a treatment of dried herbs costing just £5.00-£7.00.

Portishead
Shops

Pippin Harris 🅥

8 The Precinct, Portishead, Bristol BS20 6AH
Tel: 01275 846263 www.pippinharris.co.uk

Opening times: Monday-Saturday 9am-5pm

Farm shop selling a wide range of British products from fruit and veg to teas, coffees, juices etc both from its stores in Portishead and Weston-Super-Mare (see page 188) as well as online. Local suppliers are used where possible and many products are grown to organic standards, although may not be certificated as such.

Redland
Shops

Wild Oats Wholefoods

9-11 Lower Redland Road, Redland, Bristol BS6 6TB
Tel: 0117 973 1967 www.woats.co.uk
Opening times: Monday-Friday 9.45am-5.45pm and
Saturday 9am-5.30pm
*A great place to shop, Wild Oats offers a huge selection of
natural and organic foods as well as skincare products, food
supplements, herbs, homoeopathy and books. And if you
need help or advice just ask and you'll be dealt with in a
friendly but knowledgeable manner.*

Southville

also see neighbouring Bedminster (see page 66)

Places to eat

The Factory Café Bar ⊖Ο🌀🜂◉🜂🜂🜂

The Tobacco Factory, Raleigh Road, Southville,
Bristol BS3 1TF
Tel: 0117 902 0060 www.tobaccofactory.com

Opening times: Bar: Monday-Wednesday and Sunday
midday-11pm and Thursday-Saturday midday-midnight. Food
served: Monday-Thursday midday-3pm and 5.30-9pm, Friday-
Saturday midday-3pm and 5.30-9.30pm and Sunday midday-
4pm and 5-8.30pm

Veggie rating: 50% Vegetarian; 10% Vegan

Music/vibe: Lounge

Average cost: Tapas £2.50-£3.50/Main dishes £8-£9.50

Serving healthy Mediterranean food from its open kitchen,
The Factory Café Bar has a nice vibe and striking industrial
surrounds. Dishes include the Vegan Mezze and White
Asparagus with Piquillo & Caper Vinaigrette.

The Oasis Café ⊖Ο🜂🌀🜂🜂◉🜂🜂🜂🅿

The Southville Centre, Beauley Road, Southville,
Bristol BS3 1QG
Tel: 0117 923 1039 www.southvillecentre.org.uk

Opening times: Monday-Thursday 9am-4.15pm and Friday
9am-3.15pm

Veggie rating: 70% Vegetarian; 5% Vegan

Average cost: Sandwiches £2.90/Main dishes £4.50-£5.00

The Southville Centre is a community centre and conference centre offering a full programme of activities and classes, conference facilities, childcare and day care. The Centre also runs various community projects related to the environment, arts and older people. The Oasis Café, run from the Centre, provides visitors with a menu of hot and cold drinks, snacks and lunches, with an emphasis on healthy eating. It can also cater for a wide variety of events, and dietary requirements, on request.

Quba Ice (British & Caribbean) ⬤🦞🍴🍵🍃🍂♿

220 North Street, Southville, Bristol BS3 1JD
Tel: 0117 963 9222 www.qubaice.co.uk
Opening times: Monday-Sunday 8.45am-11pm
Veggie rating: 40% Vegetarian; 25% Vegan
Music/vibe: Caribbean, reggae, jazz, blues
Average cost: Starters £2.95-£5.95/Main dishes £6.95-£8.95
You don't need to break the bank to enjoy a taste of the Caribbean. Simply saunter along to Quba Ice and tuck into authentic Jamaican, as well as English, cuisine. On a nice day, bring your flip-flops and soak up the sun on the decked seating area else head inside. The décor is warm and inviting with mulberry walls and wooden furnishings. Dishes include Sweet Potato Korma, Chickpea Burger and Quba's Vegetarian Breakfast.

Riverside Garden Centre Café ⊖⊙⊘⊙⊙⊘⊙⊙⊗Ⓟ

Clift House Road, Southville, Bristol BS3 1RX
Tel: 0117 966 7535 www.riversidegardencentre.com

Opening times: Monday-Friday 9.30am-4.30pm, Saturday
10am-5pm and Sunday 11am-5pm

Veggie rating: 100% Vegetarian; 25% Vegan

Average cost: Soups £3.50/Paninis £3.75/Jacket potatoes
£4.50/Main dishes £5.00-£5.50

*Riverside is the only co-operative garden centre in the
country, taking root over 20 years ago and growing into a
lovely centre, with vegetarian café on-site. With lots of
seating, both indoors and out, the café provides a welcome
break away from city life and uses organic, fair-trade and
local ingredients where possible. Dishes include Celeriac &
Fennel Soup or Bangers & Root Mash with Onion Gravy.*

Teohs ⊙⊙⊙⊗⊙⊙⊙

*The Tobacco Factory, 278 North Street, Southville,
Bristol BS3 1TF*
Tel: 0117 902 1122

Opening times: Monday-Saturday midday-2.30pm and 6-11pm

Veggie rating: 80% Vegetarian & Vegan

Music/vibe: Modern

Average cost: Main dishes £6.00

*From within the Tobacco Factory – which, having been saved from
demolition, has been put to fantastic use encompassing performing
arts and entertainment, apartments, eateries and offices – Teohs
cooks up a fabulous range of Thai, Malaysian, Japanese and Chinese
dishes. And veggies can enjoy almost the entire menu as the
majority of dishes can be made using tofu. Tuck into Kajan Satay,
Yakisoba (a variation of the Chinese chow mein) and my favourite
of Pad Thai Noodle. Delicious! Also in St Agnes – see opposite.*

St Agnes
Places to eat

Teohs ⬤⬤⬤⬤⬤⬤⬤⬤

28-34 Lower Ashley Road, St Agnes, Bristol BS2 9NP
Tel: 0117 907 1191

Opening times: Monday-Saturday midday-3pm and 6-10.30pm
Veggie rating: 80% Vegetarian & Vegan
Music/vibe: Modern
Average cost: Main dishes £6.00

Enjoy a taste of the Orient at Teohs, which continues to offer great value-for-money which probably explains why it's so popular. Perfect for large groups, though can still feel surprisingly private for smaller parties and couples, Teohs' layout is similar to other Far Eastern eateries with long communal wooden tables and chairs in minimalist surrounds. Choose from the huge veggie choice on the menu, which is split into regional cuisine with spice ratings for each dish helpfully given. Also at The Tobacco Factory, Southville – see opposite.

Shops

Teohs Oriental Supermarket

28-34 Lower Ashley Road, St Agnes, Bristol BS2 9NP
Tel: 0117 907 1191

Opening times: Monday-Saturday 9.30am-6pm

Great place to buy mock meats, tofu, noodles, sushi staples and other veggie ingredients. And if you're looking for inspiration, or don't feel like cooking, then just pop next door

*and let Teohs (see previous) take the strain for you. All you
need to worry about is whether to use chopsticks or a fork!*

St Andrews
Places to eat

The Fantastic Sandwich Co ☺◉☑♿♿

*63 North Road, St Andrews, Bristol BS6 5AD
Tel: 0117 942 0470 www.fantasticsandwich.co.uk*
Opening times: Monday-Friday 8am-3pm
Veggie rating: 50% Vegetarian; 25% Vegan
Average cost: Sandwiches £1.90-£3.00
*Using bread from Herberts Bakery and salad/veg bought
each day from Bristol Fruit Market, The Fantastic Sandwich
Co rustles up a great range of sarnies for its customers,
which include business lunches, sandwich runs and outside
catering. So grab lunch to go choosing one of a wide range
of veggie fillings including Homemade Sausage with Apricot
& Ginger Chutney and Melted Mozzarella or Hummus,
Sweetcorn, Carrots, Olives & Lettuce.*

St Michaels
Places to eat

Anthem (International a La Carte) ⓥ◑◉☺☺☎♿

*27-29 St Michaels Hill, Bristol BS2 8DZ
Tel: 0117 929 2834 www.anthemrestaurant.co.uk*
Opening times: Tuesday-Saturday 6-10pm

Veggie rating: 30% Vegetarian; 10% Vegan
Music/vibe: World
Average cost: Starters £4.95/Main dishes £13.50/Desserts £4.50
*Operating from one of only a small cluster of timber framed
17th century houses (you can't miss it, it's the yellow one),
Anthem provides a truly unique dining experience. By
candlelight, diners can enjoy a menu of modern world cuisine
with veggie delights including the likes of Aduki Bean &
Apple Pâté with Fennel Seed Straws followed by Squash,
Avocado & Cardamon Stew on a Rolled Oat Base. Impressive.*

Tiffins (Gujarati) 🌐🐛🍴🍵🈸🌀🐝

*151 St Michaels Hill, Bristol BS2 8DB
Tel: 0117 973 4834 www.tiffins-bristol.co.uk*
Opening times: Monday-Saturday 4.30-9pm
Veggie rating: 80% Vegetarian; 70% Vegan
Music/vibe: Background
Average cost: Starters 50p/Main dishes £5.00/Veggie deal for
two £12.50
*For the past few years, Nick and Jay Jethway have been
cooking up a storm with their authentic Gujarati food. With
a strong emphasis on veggie dishes, which change daily,
Tiffins provide real value-for-money without forsaking
quality or taste. Largely offering a take-away service, there is
some seating available if you'd like to eat-in. Dishes include
Ondhawa (a baked snack of chickpea & rice flour), Vegetable
Curry (made with potatoes, peanut & coconut) and Chana
Dhal. You can also get a Vegetarian Tiffin for £12.50. And if
you're looking for an event caterer, Tiffins can come up
trumps, with previous clients including Buckingham Palace
and the West Indian cricket team!*

Stokes Croft
Places to eat

The Full Moon & Attic Bar ⓥ❶◗◍♿

Stokes Croft, Bristol BS1 3PR
Tel: 0117 924 5007 www.fullmoonbristol.co.uk

Opening times: The Full Moon Bar: Monday-Wednesday 9am-11pm, Thursday-Saturday 9am-12.30am and Sunday 9am-10.30pm (food served 9am-9.30pm). The Attic Bar: Monday-Wednesday 2.30-11pm, Thursday-Saturday 2.30pm-2am and Sunday 2.30pm-10.30pm

Veggie rating: 37% Vegetarian; 15% Vegan

Average cost: Light meals £4.95/Main meals £7.95

Now transformed into an eco-friendly backpacker hotel, The Full Moon is very veggie-friendly too, offering a good range of vegetarian and vegan options on its food and wine menu – which is largely organic too – as well as affordable accommodation in the city centre (just £15 for a dorm bed or £36 for a twin room per night). Whether you're looking to have a few drinks, slap-up meal or overnight stay, you'll be well catered for with two licensed bars (one traditional, the other a cocktail bar), plasma TVs, pool tables, occasional live music and outdoor courtyard.

Café Kino ⊜✪⦿①①⑤⊘⊜✪

3 Ninetree Hill, Bristol BS1 3SB
Tel: 0117 924 9200 www.cafe-kino.com

Opening times: Tuesday-Thursday 11am-5pm (food orders taken until 4pm) and Friday-Sunday 11am-9pm (food orders taken until 8pm)

Veggie rating: 100% Vegetarian (and vegan with the exception of organic dairy milk being available for tea/coffee)

Average cost: Starters £2.00-£3.00/Main dishes £3.50-£4.50/Desserts £2.00

This relatively new vegan café is a not-for-profit co-op and what's more it's just up the road from Viva!'s offices so has become a regular haunt. Firm favourites include the scrummy chocolate muffins, fit-to-burst breakfast and fantastic fresh sandwiches such as tofu salad. You can watch the world go by sitting at the window or even outside (watch your food – it's on a slope!) otherwise there's downstairs with two separate seating areas that are wonderfully cool even in the height of summer and cosy in the winter. Excellent value for money – a real gem.

The Fillin Station (Sandwich Shop) ⊜⊙✪⑩⊜⑭⊛

Unit 1 Avonmead House, 40-48 Stokes Croft,
Bristol BS1 3QD
Tel: 0117 908 7876

Opening times: Monday-Friday 8am-3pm and Saturday 10am-3pm

Veggie rating: 30% Vegetarian & Vegan

Music/vibe: Radio

Average cost: Sandwiches £2.40/Cakes £1.00

Handily situated just round the corner from the Viva! office, this place caters very well for vegans, with a separate vegan specials

103

list including not BLT but VLT (that's vegan bacon, lettuce & tomato to the uninitiated), Homemade Bean Burger and Hummus, Falafel & Carrot. There are plans to increase the range further and also include wheat and gluten-free options too. Loyalty cards are available so get on board and your card stamped to qualify for a freebie. Make sure you ask for vegan spread and mayo when you order a vegan special.

Take Five ⊖ ◎

> *72 Stokes Croft, Bristol BS1 3QY*
> *Tel: 0117 907 7502 www.takefivecafe.co.uk*

Opening times: Monday-Thursday 11am-6pm, Friday-Saturday 11am-midnight and Sunday 11am-4pm
Veggie rating: 75% Vegetarian (vegan on request)
Music/vibe: Background
Average cost: Breakfast & Lunch £4.95/Dinner £9.95
With a menu offering a selection of globally influenced dishes from Indian, Thai and Malaysian to Mexican and continental, the newly refurbished Take Five provides veggie customers with a great choice. There's Mock Duck Pasanda or Homestyle Malaysian Curry and vegans can also enjoy a mean breakfast and roast.

St Werburghs
Places to eat

The Better Food Café – see page 106

Simply Spiced (Indian Take-Away) 🅣🄿🄾🅚

88 Mina Road, St Werburghs, Bristol BS2 9XW
Tel: 0117 955 2419 www.simplyspiced.co.uk

Opening times: Tuesday-Sunday 5.30-11pm
Veggie rating: 50% Vegetarian; 30% Vegan
Average cost: Starters £2.50/Main dishes £5.00

Simply Spiced know what they're doing, with a chef at the helm with over 20 years experience cooking and preparing Indian food. Healthy eaters and allergy sufferers rejoice: no artificial colours, flavours or preservatives are used in any of their dishes and veggie, wheat-free and dairy-free options are clearly marked on the menu.

St Werburghs City Farm Café 🄾🄾🄲🄽🄾🄾🄚

Watercress Road, St Werburghs, Bristol BS2 9YJ
Tel: 0117 942 8241

Opening times: Wednesday-Sunday 10am-4pm
Veggie rating: 50% Vegetarian; 20% Vegan
Music/vibe: Background
Average cost: Main dishes £5.90

Unfortunately associated with, and directly opposite, the city farm, this café has a fantastic vibe and when you set foot inside, you'll feel like you've been transported into a fairytale as there's a slight enchanted grotto feel, with its smooth curvy wooden pillars and window frames. This place is great for the kids, with a fab play area outside complete with climbing frames, and a separate kids menu. There's lots of veggie fare, with vegan options clearly marked, and I've been told they do a great vegan breakfast.

The Better Food Co (Organic Supermarket & Café)
The Proving House, St Werburghs, Bristol BS2 9QS
Tel: 0117 935 1735 www.betterfood.co.uk
Opening times: Monday-Friday 9am-7pm, Saturday 9am-5pm
and Sunday 10am-4pm
*A fabulous organic supermarket, with an enormous range of
veggie and vegan goodies. It seems to sell everything – fruit
and veg, fresh bread, herbs, chilled and frozen products,
cereals and pulses, teas and coffees, chocolate and
confectionery, wines and spirits, cleaning products, bodycare
and even sprouters, composters, clothing and a range of
useful green gifts. If that weren't enough, there's also an on-
site café selling soups, salads and quiches, cakes and drinks.
Well worth a visit. NB: The Better Food Co is also wholesaler,
grower and supplier of a fruit and veg box scheme and The
Walled Garden Café & Shop in Wrington (see page 197).*

Shops

Sonnis Food & Wines
46 Mina Road, St Werburghs, Bristol BS2 9XJ
Tel: 0117 955 9667
Opening times: Monday-Friday & Sunday 7am-10.30pm and
Saturday 8am-10.30pm
*Surprisingly wide range of veggie/vegan foods and health
foods on offer and the later hours mean you can pick up
staples and treats on the way home from work. A godsend.*

Totterdown
Places to eat

Glasnost Restaurant (European/International)

1 William Street, Totterdown, Bristol BS3 4TU
Tel: 0117 972 0938 www.glasnostrestaurant.co.uk

Opening times: Tuesday-Thursday 7-10pm and Friday-Saturday 6.30-9.45pm

Veggie rating: 40% Vegetarian (vegan on request)

Music/vibe: Soul, swing, Motown

Average cost: 2 course £20/3 course £24

Behind Glasnost's stained glass windowed and almost cold exterior lies a vibrant and popular eatery. Its orange walls, blue flooring and tables and colourful paintings give it a warm and welcoming atmosphere. Its seasonal menus provide tasty veggie options which include the likes of Roasted Butternut Squash Soup followed by Vegetable Stroganoff (served with a platter of fresh veg) and Warm Treacle Sponge Pudding. With advance notice they will also happily cater for vegans and other special dietary requests.

Bristol-wide

Aromafoods (Vegan Snacks) Ⓢ ⊘

PO Box 111, Keynsham, Bristol BS31 2ZQ
Tel: 0800 0744 876 www.aromafoods.org.uk

Veggie rating: 100% Vegan

*Producer of a delicious range of Middle Eastern, Indian,
Japanese, Mexican, Hungarian and South East Asian snacks
available in delis across Bristol and surrounds. As well as
being 100% animal friendly, Aromafoods are also planet
friendly. In most cases less than 10 miles are covered from
production to delivery and energy efficient pots and pans
are used, as well as recycled packaging.*

Passion 4 Juice (Mobile Juice Bar) ⬤ Ⓖ Ⓢ Ⓜ Ⓥ Ⓐ Ⓖ

129A Beaufort Road, St George, Bristol BS5 8EZ
Tel: 0117 941 2505 www.passion4juice.com

Veggie rating: 98% Vegetarian; 95% Vegan

Average cost: £2.50-£5.00

*Providing wonderfully healthy smoothies and juices made
from 100% fresh pressed fruit and veg, Passion 4 Juice
provide veggie heaven for vegetarians and vegans at
festivals and events. Offering such mouth-watering delights
such as Juicy Lucy and the Passion Potion, you're sure to be
satisfied but if not, there's raw wraps and waffles to stop
those hunger pangs.*

Bath

The beautiful city of Bath attracts countless visitors every year and it's little wonder when you take a look around. It's compact enough to get about easily on foot but there's a lot to keep you occupied both day and night. From fantastically preserved historical buildings, classy shops and an extensive array of eateries, you'll have a tough choice choosing what to do first!

Bath Abbey

Top tourist attractions

Bath Abbey

Kingston Buildings, Bath BA1 1LT
Tel: 01225 422462 www.bathabbey.org

Open: April-October: Monday-Saturday 9am-6pm and Sunday 1-2.30pm and 4-5.30pm; November-March: Monday-Saturday 9am-4.30pm and Sunday 1-2.30pm

Cost: £2.50 Adult, £1.00 Child/Student (suggested contribution)

Built in 1499, Bath Abbey is the last of the great medieval churches of England. Worship has taken place on the site of the Abbey for over a thousand years, an Anglo-Saxon church and Norman cathedral formerly taking its place in 757 and 1090 respectively.

Roman Baths

Abbey Church Yard, Bath BA1 1LZ
Tel: 01225 477785 www.romanbaths.co.uk

Open: January-February: 9.30am-4.30pm, March-June: 9am-5.50pm, July-August: 9.50am-9.50pm, September-October: 9am-5pm, November-December: 9.30am-4.30pm

Cost: £10.00-£11.00 Adult, £8.50 Concession, £6.00 Child

A magnificent temple and bathing complex built by the Romans around Britain's only hot spring, that still flows to this day with natural hot water.

Royal Crescent

Bath BA1 2LR
Tel: 01225 428126 www.bath-preservation-trust.org.uk

Open: Mid-February-October: Tuesday-Sunday 10.30am-5pm

Cost: £5.00 Adult, £3.50 Concession/Child, £12.00 Family

The Royal Crescent – designed to the individual requirements of their wealthy and distinguished residents – is considered one of the finest examples of 18th century architecture. Number 1 has been designated a World Heritage Building and redecorated and furnished – using authentic materials – to show how it might have appeared in its hey-day.

Thermae Bath Spa

Hot Bath Street, Bath BA1 1SJ

Tel: 01225 331234 www.thermaebathspa.com

Open: Monday-Sunday 9am-9pm (Cross Bath) and 9am-10pm (New Royal and Hot Bath) (except Christmas Day, New Year's Eve and New Year's Day)

Cost: £12.00-£45.00

The fantastic new Bath Spa is the only place in the UK where you can bathe in natural hot waters. A combination of the best of the historic Spa with a state of the art building offering modern comforts and facilities – including four thermal baths and a full range of complementary therapies – this is a great, and extremely popular, addition to Bath's more long-standing attractions.

Tourist Information

Tourist Information Centre

Abbey Chambers, Abbey Churchyard, Bath BA1 1LY

Tel: 0906 711 2000 (50p/minute) www.visitbath.co.uk

Open: May-September: Monday-Saturday 9.30am-6pm and Sunday 10am-4pm; October-April: Monday-Saturday 9.30am-5pm and Sunday 10am-4pm

Places to stay

The Albany Guest House (4 Diamond, Silver Award)
😕 ✓ 🖉

24 Crescent Gardens, Upper Bristol Road, Bath BA1 2NB
Tel: 01225 313339 www.albanybath.co.uk

Open: Year round, except Christmas/New Year
Number of rooms: 4; En-suite: 4
Cost: £65.00-£90.00 per room/per night (special rates available low season)
Veggie breakfast: Cooked breakfast: sausages, mushrooms, tomato & egg; Toast & preserves
Vegan breakfast: As above, without egg
The Albany is ideally situated just a few minutes' walk from the city centre and a stone's throw from the Royal Crescent and Royal Victoria Park. Its owners of the past 12 years provide a warm and personal welcome to all their guests, and many return to stay time and time again. All rooms are attractively and comfortably decorated and equipped with colour television, tea/coffee making facilities, radio alarm and hairdryer.

Apsley House Hotel (AA 5 Star, Premier Collection)
😕 ○ 🖉 ○

Newbridge Hill, Bath BA1 3PT
Tel: 01225 336966 www.apsley-house.co.uk

Open: Year round, except Christmas
Number of rooms: 11; **En-suite**: 11
Cost: £70.00-£150.00 per room/per night
Views: Fabulous views over Bath Valley from most rooms
Veggie breakfast: Cooked breakfast: sausages, mushrooms,

tomato, egg & beans
Vegan breakfast: Available on request
Elegant Georgian Country House built in 1830 by the Duke of Wellington and located approximately one mile from the city centre. Refurbished to preserve elegance of bygone days, visitors will be impressed by the individually styled rooms and sumptuous furnishings. This is somewhere special to stay.

Athole Guest House (5 Star Gold Award, AA Special Breakfast Award, RAC Sparkling Diamond Award)

😊 🅞 🅐 🅖 🆂🅳 🅖🅜 🅝 🅟

33 Upper Oldfield Park, Bath BA2 3JX
Tel: 01225 320000 www.atholehouse.co.uk

Open: Year round
Number of rooms: 4; **En-suite**: 4
Cost: From £52.00 (single) and £72.00 (double) per room/ per night
Views: All rooms have garden views
Veggie breakfast: Selection of cereals and fresh muesli; Cooked breakfast; Croissants/bread with preserves; Fresh fruit salad
Vegan breakfast: Available on request
With the promise of no chintz, Athole Guest House offers a warm welcome at their restored Victorian home which is a short walk from the centre. All rooms have a range of facilities including a mini-bar and internet access.

Don't forget to mention the Vegetarian & Vegan Guide to Bristol & Bath when making an enquiry or booking!

The Belvedere Wine Vaults & B&B ● ◐ ◖◗ ✿

25 Belvedere, Lansdown Road, Bath BA1 5ED
Tel: 01225 330264 www.belvederewinevaults.co.uk
Open: Year round, except Christmas Eve/Christmas Day
Number of rooms: 4; **En-suite**: 4
Cost: From £75.00 per double room/per night (single occupancy from £50.00)
Views: Two rooms have views of Little Salisbury Hill, Twerton and Claverton Down
Veggie breakfast: Cooked breakfast: sausages, tomato, mushrooms, eggs, beans; Toast; Cereal; Yoghurt & fruit
Vegan breakfast: Available on request
It's apt that The Belvedere resides in a 17th century townhouse that was built by a man with a passion for wine, as there's an extensive wine list as well as a fantastic selection of vodkas from around the world. Offering a taste of Georgian Bath with a modern twist you can eat, drink and be merry and then retire to bed without having to set foot outside the door! There's even live music once a week. Rooms are tastefully decorated, retaining their original features, with king size beds. Food-wise, there's a daily tapas selection (served 6-10pm) and on Sundays (from midday) you can enjoy a veggie roast. Non-residents are welcome at the bar (open 5pm-midnight Monday-Wednesday, 5pm-1am Thursday-Saturday and 5-11pm Sunday) although advance notice is welcomed for groups.

Devonshire House (AA 4 Red Diamond) ⑨ ◉ ✿ ✿ ☎

143 Wellsway, Bath BA2 4RZ
Tel: 01225 312495 www.devonshire-house.uk.com
Open: Year round
Number of rooms: 4; **En-suite**: 4
Cost: From £34.00 per person

Views: Great views from two rooms
Veggie breakfast: Cooked breakfast: sausages, mushrooms, tomato, hash brown & egg
Vegan breakfast: Available on request
Devonshire House – a Victorian house built in 1880 – is located a 15 minute walk from the centre of Bath or, if travelling by car, no more than a five minute drive, with secure off-street parking provided within its walled courtyard. All rooms are en-suite and have colour television and tea/coffee trays. And if you can't trust yourself to wake up in the morning, early morning calls are available on request. Breakfast is served in the charming dining room, formerly a grocer's shop.

Lavender House (5 Diamond, Gold Award)

17 Bloomfield Park, Bath BA2 2BY
Tel: 01225 314500 www.lavenderhouse-bath.com
Open: Year round
Number of rooms: 5; **En-suite**: 4 (the other with private bathroom)
Cost: £80.00-£95.00 per room/per night for two people, £55.00-£65.00 single with private bathroom
Views: Over the Royal Crescent and surrounding hills or the garden
Veggie breakfast: Pesto toast with tomato, avocado & mozzarella
Vegan breakfast: Stuffed field mushrooms; Stuffed tomatoes; Homemade muesli or gluten-free cereal with soya or rice milk
This large Edwardian house is in a quiet conservation area overlooking Bath, just a few minutes' walk from the city centre. For guests travelling by bus or train, where possible, owners Carol and Bill Huxley will be happy to collect you. It's the purrfect place for cat lovers like myself, being home to two gorgeous kitties called Cheetah and Rosie.

Marlborough House (4 Diamond)

○ ○ ⦿ 🚭 ◐ ◑ ◒ ◓ ◔ ⊗

1 Marlborough Lane, Bath BA1 2NQ
Tel: 01225 318175 www.marlborough-house.net

Open: Year round, except Christmas Eve/Christmas Day/Boxing Day
Number of rooms: 6; **En-suite**: 6
Cost: £75.00-£125.00 per room/per night
Views: Overlooking Victoria Park and city
Veggie breakfast: Cereal; Yoghurt; Fresh Fruit; Breads, Cooked breakfast: omelette/eggs, mushrooms, tomato & potatoes
Vegan breakfast: Cereal; Soya yoghurts, Fresh Fruit; Breads; Cooked breakfast: sausages, mushrooms, tomato & potatoes
This friendly and informal hotel is located in the heart of Georgian Bath. Built in 1867, it offers six beautiful and unique rooms, each with either antique four-poster or Victorian brass and iron beds. Online/email access is also offered to guests. Marlborough House uses ecologically sound cleaning materials and provides herbal toiletries for guests' use. They are also happy to cater for vegans and other special dietary needs.

Meadowland (5 Diamond, Gold Award)

36 Bloomfield Park, Bath BA2 2BX
Tel: 01225 311079 www.meadowlandbath.co.uk

Open: Year round
Number of rooms: 3; **En-suite**: 3
Cost: £45.00-£47.50 per person
Views: Yes
Veggie breakfast: Fruit salad; Cereals/muesli; Cooked breakfast: eggs, pancake, potatoes, mushrooms & tomato

Vegan breakfast: Available on request

This B&B, set in its own grounds with off-street parking, is situated in a quiet conservation area within a 15-20 minute walk to the centre of Bath. Guests can enjoy the tranquillity of the garden in good weather or the beautifully decorated dining room which has a selection of books and magazines to read. Their three bedrooms are individually styled and have comfy beds and an abundance of pillows and cushions, tea/coffee making facilities, hairdryer, trouser press and welcoming sherry tray (!).

Millbrook (4 Diamond equivalent) 🌐🌐🌐🌐🌐🌐🌐

Waterhouse Lane, Monkton Combe, Bath BA2 7JA
Tel: 01225 723818 www.millbrookbath.com

Open: Year round
Number of rooms: 4; **En-suite**: 4
Cost: £32.50
Views: Yes, overlooking the surrounding countryside
Veggie breakfast: Cereals; Yoghurts; Fresh fruit salad; Freshly baked loaf; Cooked breakfast: sausages, free-range eggs (from their chickens), mushrooms & tomato
Vegan breakfast: As above but without yoghurts, sausage and eggs

This former Victorian farmhouse is in a designated area of outstanding beauty, with views across the valley. Just a few minutes' walk from the Kennet & Avon Canal, this is a fantastic place to explore the surrounding countryside from – and take to the water if you fancy hiring a boat or canoe for the day – and just three miles from the centre of Bath.

Number Thirty (AA 4 Star, ETC Silver 4 Star)

30 Crescent Gardens, Bath BA1 2NB
Tel: 01225 337393 www.numberthirty.com

Open: Year round
Number of rooms: 6; **En-suite**: 6
Cost: £75.00-£105.00 per double room/per night
Veggie breakfast: Cereals; Fresh fruit; Toast & jam; Cooked breakfast: for example Rosemary scented polenta with grilled tomatoes or Glamorgan sausage with tomato relish
Vegan breakfast: Available on request
Number Thirty is well situated for visitors to Bath being just five minutes' walk from the city centre and close to the Royal Crescent. All rooms have been completely refurbished and are light and airy, with one room designed particularly with allergy sufferers in mind. Colour televisions with teletext, hairdryers and tea/coffee making facilities are all provided and free email and wi-fi are also available.

The Town House (AA Red Diamond)

7 Bennett Street, Bath BA1 2QJ
Tel: 01225 422505 www.thetownhousebath.co.uk

Open: Year round, except January
Number of rooms: 3; **En-suite**: 3
Cost: £100.00-£110.00 per room per night
Views: Of Assembly Rooms
Veggie breakfast: Fruit platter; Cereals; Cooked breakfast; Croissants or home-baked muffins
Vegan breakfast: Available on request
This beautiful and unique townhouse, located in the heart of Georgian Bath, offers luxury accommodation for its guests

providing king size beds, robes, toiletries, television and radio, as well as a generous hospitality tray.

Three Abbey Green (4 Diamond, Silver Guilt Award)
Abbey Green, Bath BA1 1NW
Tel: 01225 428558 www.threeabbeygreen.com
Open: Year round, except middle two weeks of January
Number of rooms: 6; **En-suite**: 6
Cost: £85.00-£155.00 per room/per night (no singles)
Views: Beautiful views of Abbey Green
Veggie breakfast: Cereals; Cooked breakfast: Full vegetarian English
Vegan breakfast: Happy to provide vegan as well as veggie breakfast but please advise of requirements when booking
Three Abbey Green is a Grade II Listed townhouse dating back to 1689. Set in an historic square in the heart of Bath, it provides a superb central location for exploring the city. Its understated elegance is reflected in the names of its bedrooms which include Lady Hamilton, The Lord Nelson and Lilliput Court. A computer is provided for free Internet access and all rooms have wi-fi which guests can use without charge.

Don't forget to mention the Vegetarian & Vegan Guide to Bristol & Bath when making an enquiry or booking!

Places to eat

The Apple Tree (Juice Bar) ⊖ ⊘ ⟳ ⟳

> *7 Pulteney Bridge, Bath BA2 4AX*
> *Tel: 01225 443042 www.appletreejuicebar.co.uk*

Opening times: Monday-Friday 8am-5pm, Saturday 10am-5pm and Sunday 11am-4pm

Veggie rating: Juices & Smoothies: 100% Vegetarian & Vegan; Food: 80% Vegetarian; 50% Vegan

Music/vibe: Chilled/modern

Average cost: Juices & Smoothies £2.45/Food £2.60

Juices and smoothies freshly prepared and made to order, with a selection of sandwiches, cakes and organic soups and salads. After a tough day at the office or heavy night out go for the Rocket Fuel smoothie – a blend of orange, raspberry, mango & banana fruity goodness. There's a 10% discount for students.

Arabesque (Lebanese) ❶ ❶ ◎ ⟳ ⟳

> *The Podium Shopping Centre, Northgate Street,*
> *Bath BA1 5AL*
> *Tel: 01225 481333*

Opening times: Monday-Sunday midday-10.30pm

Veggie rating: Starters: 75% Vegetarian & Vegan; Mains: 20% Vegetarian & Vegan

Music/vibe: Lebanese

Average cost: Mezze £3.95/Main dishes £9.00-£12.00

Situated upstairs at The Podium, Arabesque offers a world away from the hubbub of Saturday shopping. Providing a large veggie choice of hot and cold mezze – including Baba Ghanouge, Tabouleh, Warak Inab (vine leaves), Falafel,

Fatayer Sebanikh (pastry with spinach) and two veggie main courses you can dine in Lebanese style and not go hungry. And with a special lunchtime buffet served between midday-3pm at £6.95 per person – eat as much as you like – you certainly won't!

The Bathtub Bistro (New World Cuisine)
🌐 ◐ ◖ ♿ 🄼 ◑ ◗

2 Grove Street, Bath BA2 6PJ
Tel: 01225 460593 www.bathtubbistro.co.uk
Opening times: Monday 6-11pm, Tuesday-Friday midday-2.30pm and 6-11pm, Saturday midday-11pm and Sunday midday-2.30pm and 6-11pm
Veggie rating: 45% Vegetarian (vegan on request)
Music/vibe: Jazz
Average cost: Starters £4.40/Main dishes £8.45/Desserts £4.00
The Bathtub Bistro prides itself on using fresh and high quality ingredients to create innovative dishes from around the world. There's some lovely veggie options including Roast Butternut Squash & Grilled Goat's Cheese on a Shortcrust Pastry Biscuit. Able to cater for parties of up to 60, the Bistro is spread across three candlelit rooms. And on Mondays and Tuesdays you can bring your own booze.

The Bell (Pub) ◉◉◉◉◉◉◉

103 Walcot Street, Bath BA1 5BW
Tel: 01225 460426 www.walcotstreet.com

Opening times: Monday-Saturday 11.30am-11pm and Sunday midday-10.30pm

Veggie rating: 100% Vegetarian; 30% Vegan

Music/vibe: Eclectic mix, live bands on Monday/Wednesday nights and Sunday lunchtimes

Average cost: Rolls £2.00

You'll not find a scrap of meat in this pub, which lays a nice little spread for its customers of fresh veggie rolls filled with hummus & salad or aubergine & walnut pâté, which are also vegan. There's a choice of organic and fair-trade tea, coffee and hot chocolate for those cold days snuggled up inside and in the summer head outside to the sheltered courtyard garden with a nice cooling pint.

Bombay Malay (Indian Take-Away) ◉◉◉◉◉

37 Monmouth Street, Bath BA1 2AN
Tel: 01225 480490

Opening times: Monday-Sunday 6-11.30pm

Veggie rating: 25% Vegetarian; 20% Vegan

Average cost: Starters £2.25/Main dishes £4.95

Good veggie choice here and although most have dairy – so are not on the face of it suitable for vegans – staff are prepared to adjust dishes accordingly and are generally 'allergy aware'. Another plus point is that no artificial colourings or preservatives are used. Free home delivery on orders over £10.

Boston Tea Party (Coffee House & Café)
◐◎◉◕🌓🆘◑◖◉🝐◔◔

19 Kingsmead Square, Bath BA1 2AE
Tel: 01225 313901 www.bostonteaparty.co.uk
Opening times: Monday-Saturday 7.30am-7pm and Sunday
9am-7pm
Veggie rating: 50% Vegetarian (vegan on request)
Average cost: Eat-in: Sandwiches £2.75-£3.75/Main dishes
£5.95-£6.95
The Boston Tea Party is a small independent chain of four
West Country cafés supporting local and organic suppliers
where possible and selling 100% fairly traded coffee. On
offer is a great selection of coffee, teas and sandwiches,
cakes and other light bites, many of which are veggie and
several vegan. And if your favourite food isn't on display, let
staff know and they'll make one fresh for you. Now that's
service! Seating is a bit cramped, especially by the door to
the toilet, so avoid sitting there if you can! A larger branch is
on Park Street, Bristol (see page 48).

Café du Globe (Moroccan and International)
◐◖◎◔◔◉◉◕

1A North Parade, Bath BA1 1LF
Tel: 01225 466437 www.cafeduglobe.co.uk
Opening times: Monday-Sunday 10am-10.30pm
Veggie rating: 40% Vegetarian; 10% Vegan
Music/vibe: Seventies/Eighties
Average cost: Starters £3.50-£5.50/Main dishes £6.50-£12.00
From afternoon tea to homemade pizzas and pastas and
light bites to à la carte cuisine, Café Du Globe has something
for everyone. With a Moroccan-born owner, this is
unsurprisingly their specialty and veggie delights include a

125

*Mixed Vegetable Moroccan Tagine. For a more
Mediterranean vibe, tuck into the hot panini of olive oil with
marinated tomatoes, fresh garlic, basil and black olives.*

Café Retro

18 York Street, Bath BA1 1NG
Tel: 01225 339347

Opening times: Café: Monday-Saturday 9am-6pm and
Sunday 10am-5pm. Restaurant: Tuesday-Saturday 7-10pm
Veggie rating: 30% Vegetarian; 0% Vegan
Music/vibe: Italian/French (restaurant)
Average cost: Lunch £5.00/Dinner £10.00
*Relaxed and friendly, Café Retro is a popular haunt so you
may need to fight for a seat! But once settled, you can enjoy
a choice of veggie breakfasts, hot paninis and toasties –
which include the overwhelming sounding Veggie Skyscraper
– as well as salads and other mains. Cool.*

Café Shoon ⊝🌜⊜◎🌀

14 Old Bond Street, Bath BA1 1BP
Tel: 01225 445309

Opening times: Monday-Saturday 9.30am-5pm and Sunday
11am-4pm
Veggie rating: 50% Vegetarian; 5% Vegan
Music/vibe: Gentle background music
Average cost: Sandwiches & melts £4.00-£6.00
*Shoon is a family retail business based in Wells, Somerset,
with 17 shoe shops across the country and two Shoon stores
which sell a wide range of clothing, gifts, accessories and
footwear in Bath and London. The café is up two flights of
pretty narrow stairs and although vegan options are limited,
soya milk is available, as are fair-trade items and staff are*

happy to knock up something from available ingredients. Be warned, this place gets pretty busy at lunchtimes.

California Kitchen (American) ❶ ⓪ ◎ ◎ ◎

The Podium, Northgate Street, Bath BA1 5AL
Tel: 01225 471471

Opening times: Monday-Thursday 9am-9pm and Saturday-Sunday 9am-10pm
Veggie rating: 15% Vegetarian; 0% Vegan
Music/vibe: International
Average cost: Starters £2.00-£4.25/Main dishes £5.00-£7.00
California Kitchen is just one of several eateries on the first floor of this shopping centre but there's a surprisingly high number of veggie options available here so it's a good place to grab a bite to eat mid-shop. Options include homemade soup of the day and Mediterranean Grilled Vegetables & Cous Cous.

Demuths Restaurant (World Food)
◎ ◎ ◎ ◎ ⓥ ⓢ ◎ ◎ ◎ ◎ ◎ ◎

2 North Parade Passage, Bath BA1 1NX
Tel: 01225 446059 www.demuths.co.uk

Opening times: 10am-10pm every day except Saturday 10am-9pm
Veggie rating: 100% Vegetarian; 50% Vegan
Music/vibe: World/jazz music
Average cost: Starters £5.50/Main dishes £11.50 (eve) £8.50 (day)/Desserts £5.50
A much-loved and long-established contemporary restaurant situated in the heart of Bath near The Abbey and Roman Baths, Demuths continues to impress both new and loyal customers alike. Tuck into a virtuous feast of Haloumi,

Roasted Squash & Beetroot Salad or the indulgently irresistible vegan Chocolate Fudge Cake, served warm with soya ice cream. Sheer heaven and which you can enjoy with a glass of wine from their excellent organic, vegetarian and vegan selection. You can also beat the lunchtime rush, and opt for brunch – and one of the delicious veggie breakfast options – served until 11.30am. And while you're there why not pick up one of their cookbooks or sign yourself up at their cookery school (www.vegetariancookeryschool.com) and learn how to cook the 'Demuths' way!

The Eastern Eye (Indian) 🌓 🆒 🄌 🌀 🌀 ☎

8A Quiet Street, Bath BA1 2JS
Tel: 01225 422323 www.easterneye.co.uk
Opening times: Monday-Sunday midday-2.30pm and 6-11.30pm
Veggie rating: 20% Vegetarian (vegan on request)
Music/vibe: Indian
Average cost: Starters £3.50/Main dishes £10.00
Set in a Georgian building with beautiful ceiling, this family run restaurant – which has the capacity for over 100 diners – has been visited by many celebrities over the years including actresses Jane Seymour and Brooke Shields, singer Donny Osmond, TV chef Keith Floyd and cartoonist/presenter Rolf Harris. Dishes are helpfully colour coded as to whether they contain sugar, nuts, wheat or dairy products and also how hot they are.

Feast (Pan-Asian Buffet) ⊛❶☺◐☎❺❷✪

Unit 3 Kingsmead Leisure Complex, 5-10 James Street West, Bath BA1 2BZ

Tel: 01225 333500 www.f-east.co.uk

Opening times: Monday-Thursday midday-3pm and 6-10.30pm, Friday midday-3pm and 6-11pm, Saturday midday-4pm and 5-11pm and Sunday midday-4pm and 5-10.30pm

Veggie rating: Lunch: 45% Vegetarian, Dinner: 25% Vegetarian (vegan on request)

Music/vibe: Background

Average cost: Lunch £6.50-£7.50/Dinner £13.50-£14.50

Bath's only South East Asian buffet restaurant, located next to the Odeon Cinema, where you can eat as much as you like for just one price. Feast (excuse the pun!) on Stir Fried Vegetables with Tofu or why not design your own dish and see it cooked by the chef at the Teppanyaki Grill (checking that there's no cross-contamination with the meat and fish of course!).

The Hole In The Wall (Modern British)
🌑🌀❶◐◐◐◐☎◉✪

16 George Street, Bath BA1 2EN

Tel: 01225 425242 www.theholeinthewall.co.uk

Opening times: Monday-Saturday midday-3pm and 6-10pm and Sunday 6-10pm

Veggie rating: 50% Vegetarian (vegan on request)

Music/vibe: Chilled/popular

Average cost: Starters £3.95/Main dishes £10.00/Desserts £4.00

Stylishly and simply decorated, whilst still maintaining a cosy feel, this restaurant offers its guests modern British dining themed on West Country produce. As everything is made on-site, they are happy to cater for most requests so don't be

*afraid to ask! Tasty lunches include delights such as
Mushroom, Lemon & Thyme Soup and Roast Pumpkin & Sage
Risotto with Slow Roasted Tomatoes.*

Hong Kong Bistro (Cantonese, Szechuan & Thai)
❶ ⓞ ❖ ❖ ♿

33 Southgate, Bath BA1 1TP
Tel: 01225 318500 www.hongkongbistro.co.uk

Opening times: Sunday-Thursday midday-11pm and Friday-
Saturday midday-midnight
Veggie rating: 30% Vegetarian; 20% Vegan
Music/vibe: Asian pop
Average cost: Starters £2.95/Main dishes £5.95
*Offering great Oriental food at value-for-money prices, the
owners of Hong Kong Bistro are also behind Bristol's popular
Beijing Bistro (see page 47). Specialising in Cantonese,
Szechuan and Thai cuisine, the menu is designed to offer
customers variety with over 40 main dishes – such as Thai
Style Vegetarian Curry and Mixed Vegetable & Ginger Chow
Mein – available to choose from.*

The Hop Pole (Pub) ⓞ ♿ ❶ Ⓥ ⑩ ⑤Ⓓ ⓖⓔ ◗ ◖ ⊖ ❖ ❖ ☎

Upper Bristol Road, Bath BA1 3AR
Tel: 01225 446327 www.bathales.co.uk

Opening times: Monday-Thursday and Sunday midday-11pm
and Friday-Saturday midday-midnight
Veggie rating: 10% Vegetarian & Vegan
Music/vibe: Romantic ballads
Average cost: Starters £4.95/Main dishes £10.95/Desserts £4.95
*Opposite the Royal Victoria Park and by the river, The Hop
Pole offers homemade cooking prepared to order which
means that they can cater for any special dietary*

requirements on request (notice preferred but not essential). There is always a vegan soup available and veggies can enjoy dishes such as Open Lasagne of Zucchini & Capsicums or Roasted on Vine Cherry Tomatoes, Crushed Sweet Potato & Caramelised Red Onions (which is vegan too).

Jamuna (Indian Restaurant) 🌐🌗🌕🅣🅐🛇🌑🛇🚫

9-10 High Street, Bath BA1 5AQ
Tel: 01225 464631/466626

Opening times: Monday-Thursday and Sunday midday-2.30pm and 6-11.30pm and Friday-Saturday midday-2.30pm and 6pm-12.30am

Veggie rating: 15% Vegetarian (vegan on request)

Music/vibe: Indian

Average cost: Starters £2.35/Main dishes £5.50

This large elegant restaurant resides opposite Bath Abbey and has a great view of the city. Offering superb value-for-money and customer service, Jamuna has a deserving army of admirers. Veggie choice is good, with dishes including Balti Sobji or Vegetable Massala, which are also vegan.

Java (Indonesian & Far-Eastern) 🌗🌕🅣🅐🛇🌑🚫

39 Gay Street, Bath BA1 2NT
Tel: 01225 427919 www.javarestaurant.co.uk

Opening times: Monday-Saturday midday-2.30pm and 6-11pm and Sunday 6-11pm

Veggie rating: 20% Vegetarian & Vegan

Music/vibe: Thai

Average cost: Starters £3.50/Main dishes £4.80-£5.50

Spread over two floors, Bath's first Indonesian restaurant has seating for 88 and you can keep your cool as it's air conditioned. Vegetarian dishes and spice ratings (ranging

from tingling to fiery) are clearly marked – although if unsure about any of the dishes, just ask. Also request that dishes are cooked without fish sauce to make them veggie-friendly! Tuck into the two-course lunch at £8.00 with options including Tempura Vegetables followed by Indonesian Gado Gado Salad or the three-course set dinner for £18.00 or à la carte menu which offers such delights as Gaeng Keow Wan Pak (Thai green curry with mixed vegetables, aubergine & basil). 10% off take-away.

Jazz Café 🐾🍃♿

1 Kingsmead Street, Kingsmead Square, Bath BA1 2AA
Tel: 01225 329002

Opening times: Monday-Saturday 8am-9pm and Sunday 10.30am-4pm
Veggie rating: 43% Vegetarian (vegan on request)
Music/vibe: Jazz (unsurprisingly!)
Average cost: Starters £4.75/Main dishes £6.00-£7.00/ Desserts £3.50
A bright and friendly family-run café/bistro, with a menu covering cuisine from around the world and to suit all tastes. Veggies can enjoy a large selection of dishes including Hungarian Goulash, Bean Burrito and Veggie Breakfast. Fill yer boots! Seating outside.

Juice Kitchen 🍴🍃♿

3 George Street, Bath BA1 2EH
Tel: 01225 480666

Opening times: Monday-Friday 8.30am-5.30pm, Saturday 9.30am-5.30pm and Sunday 11.30am-5pm
Veggie rating: 95% Vegetarian; 90% Vegan
Music/vibe: World, pop, folk

Average cost: £1.25-£2.50

The place to get your boosters, juices and smoothies – and power up for the day on fruit! Dairy smoothies can be made with soya milk or yoghurt but there are lots of other non-dairy options anyway such as Berry Crush with raspberry, strawberry & orange juice so get fruity!

Las Iguanas (Latin America) ◐ ❸ ❶ ◖ ◐ ◓

12 Seven Dials, Sawclose, Bath BA1 1EN
Tel: 01225 336666 www.iguanas.co.uk

Opening times: Monday-Thursday midday-11pm, Friday-Saturday midday-11.30pm and Sunday midday-10.30pm
Veggie rating: 35% Vegetarian (vegan on request)
Music/vibe: Latin American
Average cost: Starters £5.50/Main dishes £8.00/Desserts £4.00

Bright and vibrant, with a colourful frontage and décor to match (including tables with fab mosaic table tops which are made in Brazil from sustainable wood), this is a funky place to grab a bite to eat. From nachos to quesadillas and fajitas to enchiladas, there's plenty of choice and all the desserts are veggie too. And if you fancy a little tipple, relax in the bar with a cocktail. Also in Clifton and Harbourside, Bristol (see pages 35 and 59). Las Iguanas has an online store too where you can buy t-shirts, tea, coffee, sweets, alcohol, music and gift vouchers.

Don't forget to mention the Vegetarian & Vegan Guide to Bristol & Bath when making an enquiry or booking!

La Tasca (Spanish Tapas Bar & Restaurant)
🍴 🆂🅳 ⊜ ✅ ✅

36 Broad Street, Bath BA1 5LP
Tel: 01225 466477 www.latasca.co.uk
Opening times: Monday-Sunday 11am-11pm
Veggie rating: 30% Vegetarian; 10% Vegan
Music/vibe: Spanish
Average cost: Starters £2.75-£5.00/Main dishes £7.95-£9.25
Bringing the best of Spain to UK shores, and some sunshine even on the darkest of days, La Tasca serves authentic cuisine in fantastically vibrant surrounds. Tuck into speciality tapas or paella, washed down with Spanish wine, beer or Sangria. All vegetarian and gluten-free dishes are clearly marked.

Mai Thai Restaurant 🍴 🆂🅳 ⓘ 🆃🅰 ✅ ✅ ✅ 🅶

6 Pierrepont Street, Bath BA2 4AA
Tel: 01225 445557 www.maithai.co.uk
Opening times: Monday-Sunday midday-2pm and 6-10.30pm
Veggie rating: 15% Vegetarian (vegan on request)
Music/vibe: Thai
Average cost: Starters £4.00/Main dishes £5.00
Furnished with beautifully carved wooden tables and chairs, Mai Thai offers great value and deliciously authentic Thai cuisine in classy surrounds. Vegetarian options are clearly marked and include Phak Shoup (deep-fried mixed vegetables in light batter served with sweet & chilli sauce) followed by Tao Hoo Pad Tua Ngok (beancurd stir-fried with beansprouts & garlic in soy sauce). 10% discount on take-aways over £10.

Martini Ristorante (Italian) ⭕🍴🅿💷😊📞♿

8-9 George Street, Bath BA1 2EH
Tel: 01225 460818 www.martinirestaurantbath.co.uk
Opening times: Monday-Friday midday-2.30pm and 6-10.30pm, Saturday midday-10.30pm and Sunday 12.30-2.30pm and 6-10pm
Veggie rating: 20% Vegetarian; 5% Vegan
Music/vibe: Contemporary, jazz, Italian
Average cost: Starters £4.95/Main dishes £8.00-£15.00
For a true Italian night out with authentic cuisine and a friendly welcome, come to Martini. Tuck into Vegetariana Pizza or ring the changes with Penne Ercolanese (sun-dried & cherry tomatoes with black olives & rocket pesto) or Salad la Capricosa (mixed leaves, artichokes, aubergines, roasted vegetables & olives with garlic croutons in lemon oil dressing).

The Metropolitan Café ⭕🍴😊Ⓥ🍴🍴😊💷😊

15 New Bond Street, Bath BA1 1BA
Tel: 01225 482680 www.bloomsburystore.com/cafe
Opening times: Monday-Friday 9.30am-5pm, Saturday 9am-5pm and Sunday 11am-4pm
Veggie rating: 100% Vegetarian; 16% Vegan
Music/vibe: Acoustic/easy listening
Average cost: Main courses £4.00-£7.00/Desserts £2.00-£3.00
Serving a selection of wraps, melts, sandwiches and salads as well as smoothies, milkshakes and juices, this is perfect for a pit-stop whilst shopping. Just above Bloomsbury's on the corner of New Bond Street, this is a busy place but a real sanctuary in the city. Sit back with a coffee and cake or virtuous smoothie, or tuck into something more substantial such as the Mozzarella, Tomato & Fresh Basil Bruscetta with Herby Salad or Spicy Tarka Dahl served with Warm Chickpea Flatbread which is also vegan.

And if vegans fancy one of the non-vegan options just have a word with staff and they will make up something especially for you. Discount for Little Theatre members.

Number Eight (Café Bar & Gallery)
⬤⬤⬤⬤⬤⬤⬤⬤⬤⬤

8 Manvers Street, Bath BA1 1JQ
Tel: 01225 331888 www.eightmanvers.co.uk

Opening times: Monday-Thursday 8am-7pm, Friday-Saturday 8am-9pm and Sunday 10.30am-4pm

Veggie rating: 40% Vegetarian; 30% Vegan

Music/vibe: Jazz, light

Average cost: Sandwiches £2.95/Main dishes £9.95

Simply decorated in creamy and coffee tones, Number Eight is located in a refurbished group of Georgian townhouses. Providing space for local artists to showcase their work, this is a lovely place to enjoy a drink or bite to eat morning, noon or night. Vegetarians, vegans and those with special diets are more than welcome, with staff happy to adapt dishes – which include Wild Mushroom & Cherry Tomato Risotto (made with soya milk on request) and Penne Pasta with Roasted Peppers, Aubergine, Cherry Tomatoes & Pesto – to suit.

Ocean Pearl (Oriental Buffet) ⬤⬤⬤

The Podium Shopping Centre, Northgate Street,
Bath BA1 5AL
Tel: 01225 331238 www.oceanpearl-bath.co.uk

Opening times: Monday-Sunday midday-2.30pm and 6-10.30pm

Veggie rating: 30% Vegetarian (vegan on request)

Average cost: Lunch £6.00/Dinner £12.50

Decorated with bright lanterns and black cloth on the ceiling, the Ocean Pearl offers great value, especially for

*take-out (lunch/dinner boxes are available for £3.50/£4.50)
and children under 10 eating in (lunch/dinner just
£3.00/£6.00). Options include Deep Fried Onion Rings, Crispy
Seaweed and Vegetable Spring Rolls as starters followed by
Braised Cauliflower and Szechuan Beancurd and to finish
Fresh Fruit Salad. A word of warning though: some of the
food may contain GM soya/maize.*

Pasta Galore (Italian) ❶◐◍◍☎⛎

*31 Barton Street, Bath BA1 1HG
Tel: 01225 463861 www.pastagalore.co.uk*
Opening times: Monday-Sunday midday-3pm and 6-10.30pm
Veggie rating: 25% Vegetarian; 0% Vegan
Music/vibe: Opera, jazz, popular classics
Average cost: Starters £4.50/Main dishes £9.00-£10.00
*This friendly and cheerful restaurant located near the
Theatre Royal is decked out in the red, white and green of
the Italian national flag. Run by sisters Celia and Jessica, the
restaurant spans two floors and also has a courtyard area.
Expect authentically tasty Italian dishes, with pasta made
fresh on the premises every day, and a warm welcome.*

Pastiche Bistro (Modern European) ❶◐◍◍☎

*16 Argyle Street, Bath BA2 4BQ
Tel: 01225 442323 www.pastichebistro.co.uk*
Opening times: Monday-Sunday midday-2.15pm and 6.30-10pm
Veggie rating: 20% Vegetarian; 0% Vegan
Music/vibe: Soul, Motown
Average cost: 2-course lunch from £5.95/2-course dinner
from £10.95
*With views across the weir, and calming lilac walls and wooden
flooring, Pastiche provides a relaxing place to escape the crowds.*

And with a menu that changes monthly, you can try something different each time you visit. When I went there veggie options included Spicy Bean & Potato Stew with Poppadoms and Warm Hoi Sun Mushroom on Beansprout Salad.

Peking Restaurant (Cantonese, Szechuan & Peking)
() 🍵 ⚫ 😊 😊

> *1-2 New Street, Kingsmead Square, Bath BA1 2AF*
> *Tel: 01225 466377 www.pekingrestaurantbath.co.uk*

Opening times: Monday-Sunday midday-2pm and 6-11.15pm
Veggie rating: 20% Vegetarian; 10% Vegan
Music/vibe: Chinese
Average cost: Starters £3.00/Main dishes £7.50
The longest established Chinese restaurant in Bath, Peking provides a somewhat sophisticated dining experience. There are some nice veggie choices on the menu – Vegetable Spring Rolls and Aubergines in Black Bean Sauce – although don't make the mistake of ordering the Beancurd with Minced Beef which is listed alongside other veggie options! Thumbs down: Shark Fin Soup is on the menu.

The Porter (Pub)

> *2 Miles's Building, George Street, Bath BA1 2QS*
> *Tel: 01225 424104 www.theporter.co.uk/porter*

Opening times: Monday-Thursday 11.30am-midnight, Friday 11.30am-1am, Saturday 11am-1am and Sunday midday-11.30pm (food served: 11am-9pm, Sunday roast 12.30-4pm)
Veggie rating: 100% Vegetarian; 39% Vegan
Music/vibe: All sorts!!! – from jazz, soul, blues, folk and funk to festival style bands
Average cost: Main courses £5.95
Enjoy great pub grub, and good portion sizes, at The Porter.

Options include the ever-popular Shepherd's Pie (get there early to ensure there's some left for you!) as well as a full-on veggie breakfast. There's free live music on Monday-Thursday in the cellar bar, DJs on Friday and Saturday and a comedy night on Sunday, not to forget happy hour from 5.30-6.30pm. Cheers!

Pria Restaurant (Indian) 🌓⊜🔘🆃🅐🔄🔄

4A Argyle Street, Bath BA2 4BA
Tel: 01225 462323/442955 www.priarestaurant.co.uk
Opening times: Monday-Thursday and Sunday 6pm-1.30pm and Friday-Saturday 6pm-2am
Veggie rating: 10% Vegetarian & Vegan
Music/vibe: Indian
Average cost: Starters £1.95/Main dishes £4.95
This popular restaurant is a bit limited on veggie eats but a good place to come if you're out and about late in Bath. Vegetarians and vegans alike can enjoy the Vegetable Biriani – one of my favourites – and if you're a student you can take advantage of a 10% discount.

P'zazz 🔘🔄⊜🅣🅐🔄

1 Grove Street, Bath BA2 6PJ
Tel: 01225 425888
Opening times: Monday-Saturday 10am-7.30pm
Veggie rating: 60% Vegetarian; 10% Vegan
Average cost: Salads £1.50/Pizzas £2.75-£3.75
Freshly made to order using their own organic dough, P'zazz offerings include some great pizzas, salads and cakes to go. Try the Coker (thyme, lemon & garlic marinated artichoke with roasted peppers topped with parmesan and rocket) or Moroccan (cumin, coriander & chickpea base brushed with garlic olive oil topped with hummus, tzatziki & salsa pine nuts).

The Rajpoot (Indian) ⭕🌀🌑🔾🅐🌑🌑🌑🌀

4 Argyle Street, Bath BA2 4BA
Tel: 01225 466833/464758 www.rajpoot.co.uk

Opening times: Monday-Thursday and Sunday midday-2.30pm and 6-11pm and Friday-Saturday midday-2.30pm and 6-11.30pm

Veggie rating: 35% Vegetarian (vegan on request)

Music/vibe: Indian/Bangladeshi

Average cost: Starters £2.75/Main dishes £6.95

Just across the river from the city centre, The Rajpoot has been divided up to provide customers with three very different areas to dine – The Old India, India Cottage and Kamra – each with its own décor and character. There are seven vegetarian specialities on the menu which include Rajpoot Vegetables and Sobji Massala (which is also vegan).

Raphael's Bar & Restaurant (Parisian & European cuisine) ⭕🌑🕅🔾🌑🌑🌑🌑

Gascoyne House, Upper Borough Walls, Bath BA1 1RN
Tel: 01225 480042 www.raphaelrestaurant.co.uk

Opening times: Monday-Saturday 11am-11pm and Sunday midday-10.30pm

Veggie rating: 10% Vegetarian (vegan on request)

Music/vibe: Lounge/smooth jazz

Average cost: Starters £4.50-£5.95/Main dishes £9.25-£12.95

For somewhere a little classy, and perfect for those pre- and post-theatre hunger pangs, Raphael ticks all the boxes with its dark polished floors, brasserie tables and modern art. But you don't need to break the bank to eat here – go for the set lunch and dine on tasty veggie delights such as Russian Salad followed by Roasted Vegetable Gratin.

Sally Lunn's (English) 🐄🍷🕸🛍🎵🌀🍴☎

Sally Lunn's House, 4 North Parade Passage, Bath BA1 1NX
Tel: 01225 461634 www.sallylunns.co.uk

Opening times: Monday-Friday 10am-9.30pm, Saturday
10am-10pm and Sunday 11am-9pm

Veggie rating: 48% Vegetarian; 10% Vegan

Music/vibe: Classical

Average cost: Starters £4.00/Main dishes £6.00/Desserts £4.00

Where better to enjoy a cuppa and a toasted bun than the
oldest house in Bath (est. 1680) made famous by Sally Lunn, a
young French refugee, for her buns. Or if you're feeling a
little more peckish, try the Roasted Root Vegetables with
Sun-dried Tomato Toasted Sandwich or the Soup (also vegan).
And for afters you can visit the museum in the cellars (free to
customers), where you can see not only the Roman and
Medieval foundations of the house and the original kitchen
used by Sally Lunn but the stalactite and stalagmite cellar.

Schwartz Bros (Burger bar) 🌀🍴🕸🌀🌀🌀

4 Sawclose, Bath BA1 1EY
Tel: 01225 461726

Opening times: Monday-Wednesday midday-midnight,
Thursday midday-12.30am, Friday midday-1am, Saturday
11.30am-1am and Sunday midday-11pm

102 Walcot Street, Bath BA1 5BG
Tel: 01225 463613

Opening times: Monday midday-10.30pm, Tuesday midday-
11.30pm, Wednesday-Thursday midday-midnight, Friday
midday-12.30am, Saturday 11.30am-12.30am and Sunday
midday-10.30pm

Veggie rating: 36% Vegetarian (NB: veggie burgers are also vegan)

Average cost: £2.80-£3.70

Sometimes you just fancy a burger and when you do head to Schwartz for 'the best in Bath'. Open until the early hours you know you won't go hungry even after a night down the pub. The veggie burgers are vegan so are suitable for all but just make sure you order without the cheese and mayo.

Shakeaway ⬤ 🆂🅳 ⬤ 🆃🅰

3 Beau Street, Bath BA1 1QY
Tel: 01225 466200 www.shakeaway.com

Opening times: Monday-Friday 9.30am-5.30pm, Saturday 9am-6pm and Sunday 10.30am-5pm
Veggie rating: 38% Vegetarian; 25% Vegan
Average cost: Regular shake £2.50/Large £3.60 (add 99p/£1.49 for organic soya milk/ice cream)
One of eight, with a branch also in Bristol (see page 26), Shakeaway provides a great choice for veggies clearly marking on their extensive menu vegetarian, vegan and gluten-free options. Organic soya milk or dairy-free ice cream is available at an extra charge and regular milkshakes can also be hot (some flavours may be better suited to this than others!). Now what to choose – from cucumber to coffee, mandarin to maple syrup and strawberries to sesame snaps, there really is something for everyone!

Thai Balcony Restaurant 🄽 🅞 🆃🅰 🔄 ⬤ 🅜 ♿

1 Seven Dials, Sawclose, Bath BA1 1EN
Tel: 01225 444450

Opening times: Monday-Sunday midday-2.30pm and 6-11pm
Veggie rating: 20% Vegetarian; 10% Vegan
Music/vibe: Thai
Average cost: Starters £4.75/Main dishes £5.95
You might've turned your back on 'chicken in a basket' but

what about the upmarket veggie version of Thai Balcony in a Basket which is made up of vegetables, deep-fried with tempura batter served in a noodle basket?! There's a good selection so, if you can't decide, simply opt for the set menu at £17.95 and just wait for a veggie feast to be brought to your table. A fine dining experience in beautifully decorated surrounds. Also 10% discount on take-away.

Tilleys Bistro (French, Mediterranean & English)
〇❶🆂🅳🌀🌀☎🦽

3 North Parade Passage, Bath BA1 1NX
Tel: 01225 484200 www.tilleysbistro.co.uk
Opening times: Monday-Saturday midday-2.30pm and 6.30-10.30pm
Veggie rating: 30% Vegetarian; 15% Vegan
Music/vibe: French, classical, sixties, modern
Average cost: Lunch: £11.00 2 course and £13.50 3 course. Evening: Starters £6.00/Main dishes £9.00/Desserts £6.00
Spread across three floors, with a basement and ground floor restaurant as well as a function room available for private hire on its first floor, Tilleys offers a French biased but varied menu. There's a good choice for veggies with options including Olives & Freshly Baked Ciabatta for two and Wild Mushroom Pancake.

Don't forget to mention the Vegetarian & Vegan Guide to Bristol & Bath when making an enquiry or booking!

The Walrus & The Carpenter Restaurant (English)

28 Barton Street, Bath BA1 1HH
Tel: 01225 314868

Opening times: Monday-Saturday midday-2.30pm and 6-11pm, Sunday midday-11pm

Veggie rating: 50% Vegetarian; 10% Vegan

Average cost: Starters £4.00-£5.00/Main dishes £8.00-£12.00/Desserts £4.00-£5.00

Family-run restaurant, with a second establishment in Clifton, Bristol (see page 45). All meals are homemade using small local suppliers and organic or locally sourced produce. Separate vegetarian menu available, with dishes such as Spinach Lasagne, Nut Loaf with Mushroom & Watercress Sauce or Mushroom Moussaka for vegetarians and Nut Loaf with Tomato & Basil Sauce for vegans.

The Wife of Bath Restaurant (Modern British)

12 Pierrepont Street, Bath BA1 1LA
Tel: 01225 461745 www.wifeofbathrestaurant.co.uk

Opening times: Monday-Saturday midday-2pm and 5.30-10.30pm and Sunday 5-10pm

Veggie rating: 25% Vegetarian

Music/vibe: Quiet pop/classical

Average cost: Starters £4.00/Main dishes £10.00/Desserts £4.80

Named after one of the characters in Chaucer's Canterbury Tales, this family-run restaurant spans five rooms to provide plenty of space as well as cosy corners which are perfect for couples and girlie chats. The walled patio, complete with fountain, is perfect for sunny days and warm evenings. Although sadly no choice for vegans (except perhaps the side orders), vegetarians can tuck into various dishes including freshly homemade soup and Spicy Chick Pea & Aubergine Stew with Basmati Rice. Thumbs down: kangaroo meat is on the menu.

Yak Yeti Yak (Nepalese) ⭕️🌀🕐️🌐️🅰️🔄️😊☎️

12 Argyle Street, Bath BA2 4BQ
Tel: 01225 442299 www.yakyetiyak.co.uk
Opening times: Monday-Thursday and Sunday midday-2pm and 6-10pm and Friday-Saturday 6-10.30pm
Veggie rating: 55% Vegetarian; 50% Vegan
Music/vibe: Traditional Nepalese
Average cost: Starters £3.50/Main dishes £3.90/Desserts £2.90
Very friendly and family-run restaurant specialising in authentic Nepalese food, where you can dine on traditional floor cushions or the more conventional tables and chairs. Great variety of veggie food, all of which is made freshly on the premises. Go for the set menu at £10.50 or choose from starters and main dishes including Aloo Dum (spiced potato & sesame salad in a popadum basket) and Aloo Tamar (fermented bamboo shoot stir-fried with new potatoes & black-eye peas) finished off with Freak Street Apples, a spiced apple tart. Or if there's eight or more of you, why not take control and get your very own tailor-made set menu to suit your requirements. 10% discount for take-away Monday-Thursday.

Yum Yum Thai ⬤🐄🍴🅥🅜🍶🍵🅣🅐🍲🍷🐸🅟

17 Kingsmead Square, Bath BA1 2AE
Tel: 01225 445253
Opening times: Monday-Saturday midday-2.30pm and
6-11pm and Sunday 6-11pm
Veggie rating: 75% Vegetarian (vegan on request)
Music/vibe: Thai/jazz
Average cost: Main dishes £8.95
Offering a good choice for veggies, this informal and modern
restaurant can also adapt other dishes on request so don't forget
to ask! Otherwise opt for one of their most popular dishes –
Vegetable Green Curry & Rice. Also in Bristol (see page 50).

Shops

Aveda

At Jolly's Bath, 7-13 Milsom Street, Bath BA1 1DD
Tel: 08701 607224 www.aveda.co.uk
Opening times: Monday-Wednesday and Friday 9.30-6pm,
Thursday 9.30am-7pm and Saturday 11am-5pm
At Artizan Hair Salon, Bartlett Street Tel: 01225 420611
and George Street
Opening times: Monday and Wednesday 9am-5.30pm, Tuesday
9am-5pm, Thursday-Friday 9am-6pm and Saturday 9am-5pm
Aveda offers a range of upmarket and largely plant-based
and organic hair care, skincare, perfume and make-up – with
prices to match, but I've been told well worth it. As well as
being animal-friendly, they're also environmentally and
ethically friendly too, aiming to offer fair deals for suppliers
and produce products that are safe for the earth as well as
the people using them.

Chandni Chowk

6 New Bond Street Place, Bath BA1 1BH
Tel: 01225 484700 www.chandnichowk.co.uk
Opening times: Monday-Saturday 9.30am-5.30pm
Ethical fair-trade shop selling rugs, curtains, throws, clothing, jewellery and gifts. Also in Bristol. Chandni Chowk specialises in textiles handmade in India and Bangladesh by skilled craftspeople. Unfortunately some are silk/wool based but there are cotton versions of many.

Chandos Deli

12 George Street, Bath BA1 2EH
Tel: 01225 314418 www.chandosdeli.com
Opening times: Monday-Saturday 9am-5pm
As well as the usual deli options which include olives, roasted peppers and the like, there's also some lovely vegan sandwich choices available. This branch of Chandos Deli also has a small café area so you can eat in too.

Click Internet Café

13A Manvers Street, Bath BA1 1JH
Tel: 01225 481008 www.clickcafe.zen.co.uk
Opening times: Monday-Sunday 10am-10pm
Handily placed by the bus and train stations, this internet café offers high speed web access so don't wait around between connections, why not catch up on emails or surf the net instead?

Culpeper

28 Milsom Street, Bath BA1 1DG
Tel: 01225 425875 www.culpeper.co.uk
Opening times: Monday-Saturday 9am-6pm and Sunday 11am-5pm
Culpeper sells a range of natural and beneficial herbal products for the bath, body and home as well as aromatherapy and essential oils, food and drink, herbs and tinctures, accessories, gifts and books. Personal favourites include the soya wax candles and range of aromatherapy oils, perfect for creating my very own blends (including insect repellent!).

Deli Shush

8 Guildhall Market, High Street, Bath BA2 4AW
Tel: 01225 425640
Opening times: Monday-Saturday 8am-5.30pm
Just inside the entrance to the Guildhall Market, this small deli offers some good veggie nibbles – around 25% – including olives, marinated vegetables and pulses, spicy snacks and filled rolls. Shame some of them are scarily close to meat products also on sale!

Dr China

12A Union Street, Bath BA1 1RR
Tel: 01225 442886 www.drchina.co.uk
Opening times: Monday-Saturday 9.30am-6pm
Nationwide, with more than 60 stores across the country including at Weston-Super-Mare (see page 186), Dr China offers herbal medicines as well as acupressure, acupuncture, massage, cupping, reflexology, beauty therapy and heat treatment. You can get a free consultation so if something's troubling you, why not drop in?

Eureka Trading Co

9 High Street, Bath BA1 5AQ
Tel: 01225 462259 www.eurekatrading.co.uk
Opening times: Monday-Friday 9.30am-6pm, Saturday 9am-6pm and Sunday 11am-5pm
A family-run shop, Eureka specialises in working with artisans and producers in Indonesia, Thailand, India and Poland. As well as their Bath store, they have an online shop, both of which sell a wide range of beautiful jewellery, bags, scarves, sarongs, drums, woodcarvings and hammocks.

Fopp

Unit 5-10 Westgate Buildings, Bath BA1 1EB
Tel: 01225 473830 www.fopp.co.uk
Opening times: Monday-Saturday 9am-6pm, Sunday 11am-5pm
From humble beginnings, Fopp has grown to become Britain's largest independent chain of music stores. But there's not just music – you can also buy films and books and, while you're browsing, take five and have a coffee, with soya milk too! There's also a branch with a café on Whiteladies Road, Bristol (see page 63).

GNC

Southgate Centre, Bath BA1 1TD
Tel: 01225 471093 www.gnc.co.uk
Opening times: Monday-Saturday 9am-5.30pm and Sunday 10.30am-4.30pm
You usually expect to find various health supplements and hulking great jars of whey protein and the like to beef up bodybuilders at GNCs and although there's more of the same here, there's also a wider choice than most with a selection

*of vegan chocolate as well as a chiller cabinet packed with
veggie burgers, dairy-free ice cream etc.*

Greenhouse

  4 Shires Yard, Milsom Street, Bath BA1 1BZ
  Tel: 01225 471400 www.greenhouseonline.co.uk
Opening times: Monday-Saturday 9.30am-5.30pm and
Sunday 11am-4pm
*Being green just got classy! Greenhouse sells a range of
items from jewellery to bags and stationery to furniture, all
of which are low on environmental impact but high on style.
Operating from its shops in Bath and Truro, Cornwall, as well
as online store, everything sold is recycled.*

Harvest

  37 Walcot Street, Bath BA1 5BN
  Tel: 01225 465519 www.harvest-bath.coop
Opening times: Monday, Wednesday-Saturday 9am-6pm and
Tuesday 10am-6pm
*Vegetarians and vegans are spoilt for choice in this health
food haven. There's a fantastic choice of products, as well as
organic fruit and veg, weigh your own seeds, pulses and
muesli, fresh breads and a great take-away range. In
business since 1971, and part of the Essential Trading Co-
operative, this is a long-established and well-deserved
favourite. Also in Gloucester Road, Bristol (see page 76).*

Holland & Barrett

  42 Stall Street, Bath BA1 1QH
  Tel: 01225 330812 www.hollandandbarrett.com
Opening times: Monday-Saturday 9am-5.30pm and Sunday
11am-5pm

Situated in the main drag, just across from the Roman Baths, this high street favourite has the usual choice of snacks as well as take-away pasties and veggie sausage rolls – made with non-hydrogenated fats – in the chiller cabinet.

Julian Graves

Unit 1, The Podium Centre, Northgate Street, Bath BA1 5AL
Tel: 01225 448404 www.juliangraves.co.uk
Opening times: Monday-Saturday 9am-6pm and Sunday 11am-5pm
Another regular, packed with nuts and all sorts of other nibbles (a personal fave are the chilli crackers, although watch the calories!). Get munching!

London Road Food Co-op

Riverside Community Centre, York Place, London Road, Bath
Tel: 07837 784715 www.organico-op.org
Opening times: Wednesday 4-7pm
Started in 2001 as a healthy eating project to encourage people to eat better food, the not-for-profit London Road Food Co-op has evolved into a weekly shop selling local, organic, fair-trade and environmentally friendly groceries to its members. Vegetable boxes can be ordered, as well as wholefoods from local producers. 100% veggie.

Lush

12 Union Street, Bath BA1 1RR
Tel: 01225 428271 www.lush.co.uk
Opening times: Monday-Friday 9.30-5.30pm, Saturday 9am-6pm and Sunday 11am-5pm
Perfectly named, just walking past Lush sends you into an instant high as lovely aromas pour out on to the streets and fill

151

the air. 100% vegetarian, with a high proportion of products also vegan, this place is fantastic for soaps, shampoos, cleansers, face masks and a mind-boggling choice of bath bombs. Heaven scent! Also in Broadmead, Bristol (see page 27).

National Trust Shop

Marshall Wade's House, Abbey Churchyard, Bath BA1 1LY
Tel: 01225 460249

Opening times: Monday-Saturday 9am-5.30pm and Sunday 11am-5pm

Opposite the Roman Baths and the Abbey, this is a good place to buy gifts such as books (including wildlife), practical and decorative glassware and pottery, chutney, biscuits and more. You can also buy a great big chocolate marzipan bar that's vegan for £1.50 – perfect to share!

Neal's Yard Remedies

7 Northumberland Place, Bath BA1 5AR
Tel: 01225 466944 www.nealsyardremedies.com

Opening times: Monday-Saturday 9.30am-5.45pm and Sunday 11am-5pm

As well as offering natural treatments and therapies, Neal's Yard also offers a wide range of kind and gentle beauty and body products – much of it organic – in-store as well as online.

New Leaf Healthfoods

29 Shaftesbury Road, Oldfield Park, Bath BA2 3LJ
Tel: 01225 425301

Opening times: Monday-Friday 9.30am-5.30pm and Saturday 9am-5pm

It's nice to see another independent in town so if you're in the neighbourhood do check it out. There's a wide range of

vegetarian and vegan health foods and cruelty-free products on offer.

Oxfam

    12A George Street, BA1 2EH
    Tel: 01225 464838
Opening times: Monday-Saturday 9.30am-4.30pm
    12 Argyle Street, Bath BA2 4BQ
    Tel: 01225 466798
Opening times: Monday-Saturday 9.30am-4.30pm
Whilst we don't approve of its projects to 'help' the developing world by providing its people with goats, chickens and other animals, Oxfam does nonetheless do some good work which you can support, and get a little something for yourself by snapping up a second-hand bargain (also helping the planet!) or buying products from the range of fair-trade goodies. I love the Divine dark chocolate bar!

Seasons

    10 George Street, Bath BA1 2EH
    Tel: 01225 469730
Opening times: Monday-Friday 9am-5.30pm and Saturday 9.30-5.30pm
This is a bit of a Tardis shop which, just when you think you've reached its depths, stretches further back with shelves packed full of pulses and grains. Up until that point you walk through rows of natural remedies, toiletries and even hair dyes as well as a good choice of health foods and chilled products. By the counter there's also a great range of take-away items.

Superdrug

42 Southgate Street, Bath BA1 1TG
Tel: 01225 331338

Opening times: Monday-Saturday 8.30am-5.30pm and Sunday 10.30am-4.30pm

31-32 Westgate Street, Bath BA1 1EL
Tel: 01225 421680

Opening times: Monday-Saturday 8.30am-5.30pm and Sunday 11am-5pm

It can be pretty tough to find cruelty-free and vegan cosmetics on the high street, hence this listing. At Superdrug you can buy Barry M cosmetics, all of which are vegetarian. Vegans should avoid the Foundation Crème, Shimmering Body Crème, Translucent Compact, Natural Dazzle Compact, Shimmering Eye and Lip Crayon, Lip Paint, Lip Gloss and Mascara. With a wide choice of Dazzle Dust pots in just about every colour of the rainbow, you can really razzle dazzle 'em!!

TUMI (Latin American Crafts)

8-9 New Bond Street Place, Bath BA1 1BH
Tel: 01225 446025 www.tumi.co.uk

Opening times: Monday-Saturday 9.30am-6pm and Sunday 11am-5pm

Born out of the founder's love of Latin America, TUMI's range – available online as well as in-store – has grown over the years to include a wide variety of colourful home furnishings, beautiful jewellery and clothing. Perfect for a gift, look out for the funky Mexican tin clocks and beautiful frosted glass capelas. You'll have a job choosing something from the fantastic range of jewellery, although watch out as some are made with shell.

Bradford-on-Avon

Bradford-on-Avon is a small picturesque historic town, just eight miles from Bath, which still bears the wealth of the local wool and cloth industry from past times. Walking its pretty streets you will clearly see the fine stone houses of well-to-do merchants and, up on the hillside, rows of smaller weavers' cottages. For its size, there are lots of places to eat and drink and it really is a lovely place to spend some time, especially on a sunny day when you can also enjoy a walk along the Kennet & Avon Canal, a short stroll from town.

© Rob Hill

Bradford-on-Avon town bridge

Tourist information

Tourist Information Centre

50 St Margarets Street, Bradford-on-Avon BA15 1DE
Tel: 01225 865797 www.bradfordavon.com

Open: April-October: Monday-Sunday 10am-5pm; November-March: Monday-Saturday 10am-4pm and Sunday 10am-3pm

Places to stay

Bradford Old Windmill (5 Diamond)

4 Masons Lane, Bradford-on-Avon BA15 1QN
Tel: 01225 866842 www.bradfordoldwindmill.co.uk

Open: March-October
Number of rooms: 3 **En-suite**: 3
Cost: £39.00-£54.50 per person per night; set dinner £24.00 per person (served 8pm)
Views: Yes
Veggie breakfast: 100% vegetarian
Vegan breakfast: Devilled mushrooms on wholemeal muffins
Enjoy an unusual but memorable stay in Bradford's only windmill, tucked on the hillside amongst the trees. Deliberate over which room to stay in, choosing between the 'Damsel' room at the top of the building with its conical ceiling and water bed, the 'Great Spur', a 19ft room with round bed and gothic windows or the 'Fantail Suite' boasting its own sitting room and bathroom, high ceiling, gothic iron bed and spectacular views. And you can stay in of a night enjoying dinners of varying cuisine – Nepali,

Mexican, Thai, Caribbean, Mediterranean – which can be provided on request.

Places to eat

The Bridge Tea Rooms ⊖⊖⊕⊕⊕⊕⊗⊕⊕

24A Bridge Street, Bradford-on-Avon BA15 1BY
Tel: 01225 865537

Opening times: Wednesday-Saturday 9.30am-5pm and Sunday midday-5.30pm

Veggie rating: 33% Vegetarian (vegan on request)

Music/vibe: Victorian, harp

Average cost: Soups £4.95/Specials £10.95

Just by the river and situated in one of the most fantastic buildings of Bradford-on-Avon dating back to 1675, this is the perfect place for tea and cake (or award winning cream tea), brought to you by staff dressed in Victoria costume. Vegans and the dairy intolerant can have soya or rice milk and food-wise, vegan options can be made to order, as everything is made fresh on the premises.

The Canal Tavern (Pub & Restaurant)
⊖⊕⊕⊕⊕⊕⊕⊕⊕⊕⊕⊕⊕⊕

49 Frome Road, Bradford-on-Avon BA15 1LE
Tel: 01225 867426

Opening times: Monday-Sunday 10am-midnight

Veggie rating: 20% Vegetarian (vegan on request)

Music/vibe: Easy listening

Average cost: Starters £4.50/Main dishes £8.50/Desserts £3.95

Just opposite the Lock Inn Café (see opposite) next to the canal, this pub is vegetarian and vegan friendly, with some

tasty options such as Mushroom Stroganoff, Mediterranean Quiche and Veggie Chilli (also vegan). But if those don't take your fancy, don't worry – just let them know in advance and they'll knock up something else for you. Ah, if only other places were so accommodating.

The Cottage Co-operative (Organic Vegetarian Café)
😀😀🌑🌀😀

33 Silver Street, Bradford-on-Avon BA15 1JX
Tel: 01225 867444

Opening times: Monday-Saturday 10am-5.30pm (Winter closing 5pm)
Veggie rating: 100% Vegetarian; 50% Vegan
Average cost: Soups £3.50/Rolls £2.75/Main dishes £4.95
This is a lovely little veggie café, with seating available outside in the peaceful courtyard. Choose from a selection of dishes – which are organic where possible – including soups, rolls, salads, cakes and drinks. For a veggie establishment I'd hoped there'd be more tempting vegan fare (which aren't always marked so check first) but you can't have everything. The hearty soups and tasty chocolate cake – if you're lucky enough to have – more than make up for it.

The Lock Inn Café 😀😀🌑🌀😀😀🌀

48 Frome Road, Bradford-on-Avon BA15 1LE
Tel: 01225 868068 www.thelockinn.co.uk

Opening times: Monday 8.45am-6pm, Tuesday-Wednesday 8.45am-11pm, Thursday-Saturday 8.45am-11.30pm and Sunday 8.45am-7pm
Veggie rating: 24% Vegetarian; 10% Vegan
Average cost: Main dishes £6.00-£7.00
This is a very popular place, especially in the summer, and is

ideally situated right next to the canal. You can watch the watery world go by – colourful canal boats, day cruisers and canoes, many of which moor up and stop for lunch, as well as an abundance of wildlife including ducks, swans, coots, moorhens, dragonflies, butterflies and, if you're lucky, water voles. You can even take to the water yourself – the café hire boats as well as bikes, on which you can explore the surrounding towpaths – a fantastic way to spend the afternoon (tel 01225 867187 for details). Veggie options, which come in good sized portions, include the Veggie Boatman's Breakfast, Jacket Potatoes with Mushrooms, Beans, Cheese or Sweetcorn, Veggie Samosas or Veggie Jambalaya.

Maharaja Tandoori Restaurant ❶ ◎ ⓐ ◐ ◐ ☎ ⬤

12 Frome Road, Bradford-on-Avon BA15 1LE
Tel: 01225 866424

Opening times: Sunday-Thursday 6-11pm and Friday-Saturday midday-2pm and 6-11.30pm
Veggie rating: 20% Vegetarian; 19% Vegan
Music/vibe: Indian
Average cost: Starters £3.00/Main dishes £5.50
A very nice Indian restaurant offering a good selection of vegetarian and vegan dishes so you can slowly work your way through the menu each time you visit!

Mr Salvats Coffee Room ◐ ◎ ◐

44 St Margarets Street, Bradford-on-Avon BA15 1DE
Tel: 01225 867474

Opening times: Thursday-Sunday 10am-5pm
Veggie rating: 35% Vegetarian; 3% Vegan
Average cost: Starters £2.50/Main dishes £3.00-£4.00
A relaxing place to spend some time – in the secluded

garden in the summer or in front of the fire in the winter of this 17th century period coffee room. There's a limited menu choice but vegetarians and vegans can tuck into a jacket potato washed down with tea, coffee or hot apple juice with cinnamon, served by staff wearing period clothing.

Rialto Ristorante (Italian) 🔵🔵🔵🔵🔵🔵

9-10 St Margarets Street, Bradford-on-Avon BA15 1DA
Tel: 01225 862123

Opening times: Monday, Wednesday-Saturday midday-2pm and 6-10pm and Tuesday 6-10pm
Veggie rating: 25% Vegetarian (vegan on request)
Music/vibe: Classical Italian
Average cost: Starters £5.50/Main dishes £8.00/2-course lunch £10.00

Authentic Italian restaurant, which you'll find as you head out of town towards the river. There's some tasty veggie options on offer, such as Griglata Ortolana (grilled mixed vegetables with goat's cheese) and there's also the usual pasta and pizza dishes we've come to love and expect too!

The Thai Barn 🔵🔵🔵🔵🔵

24 Bridge Street, Bradford-on-Avon BA15 1BY
Tel: 01225 866443 www.thai.4value.co.uk

Opening times: Tuesday 6-11pm, Wednesday-Sunday midday-2pm and 6-10pm
Veggie rating: 17% Vegetarian (vegan on request)
Music/vibe: Thai
Average cost: Starters £4.95/Main dishes £5.95-£6.50

Dine in true Thai style at The Thai Barn, where staff serve you in traditional dress and you're surrounded by authentic décor. You can choose from a variety of tasty veggie dishes from Kratong Tong (golden pastry cups filled with mixed vegetables & ground peanuts & cashew nuts) or Chu Chi Tofu (tofu in rich red curry sauce with cherry tomatoes, pineapple & kaffir lime leaves). A classy place.

Shops

Bishopston Trading Co Ltd

33 Silver Street, Bradford-on-Avon BA15 1JX
Tel: 01225 867485 www.bishopstontrading.co.uk

Opening times: Monday-Saturday 9.30am-5pm
Bishopston Trading, which has five shops across the region as well as a mail order catalogue, was set up as a fair trade worker's co-operative. Designed to create employment in the south Indian village of K V Kuppam, it has established links with Bishopston in Bristol. The main fabrics used are organic handwoven cotton, calico and denim and there are some great pieces such as shirts, bags and jewellery. Get the feel good factor and buy a little something for yourself or as a present.

The Cottage Wholefoods

33 Silver Street, Bradford-on-Avon BA15 1JX
Tel: 01225 866590

Opening times: Monday-Saturday 9am-5pm
This great little wholefood shop packs a punch for its size, offering a wide range of products – vegetarian and vegan – including beers, wines and spirits, take-away pies and pasties, fresh bread, toiletries and natural remedies, chilled and frozen convenience foods and the usual staples you'd expect to see in a good wholefood shop.

The Earth Collection

5 Market Street, Bradford-on-Avon BA15 1LH
Tel: 01225 868876 www.theearthcollection.com

Opening times: Monday-Saturday 10am-5pm

It is increasingly possible to buy environmentally friendly clothing, and at an affordable price, as The Earth Collection demonstrates. Displaying a variety of colour co-ordinated separates, the shop sells 100% cotton and cotton-mix garments. Unfortunately it also sells several items made from cotton/silk mix – not sure if it's these which give the store an interesting aroma!

Inspiration Holistic Centre ✪

8 Market Street, Bradford-on-Avon BA15 1LH
Tel: 01225 866470 www.inspirationholisticcentre.co.uk

Opening times: Tuesday-Friday 10.30am-4.30pm and Saturday 10.30am-5.30pm

If you need to unwind, de-stress or basically sort yourself out, this is the place to come! A variety of holistic and beauty treatments are on offer to suit all, including facials, aromatherapy, reflexology, Indian head massage, reiki, manicures, pedicures, waxing and lots more besides as well as a complete range of crystals, candles, spells, books, CDs, jewellery, incense, oils, herbal teas, angels, faeries and skincare. And r-e-l-a-x!

Maples Delicatessen

4 The Shambles, Bradford-on-Avon BA15 1JS
Tel: 01225 862203

Opening times: Monday-Wednesday 8am-6pm, Thursday-Friday 8am-6.30pm and Saturday 8am-5.15pm

This deli sells all sorts of scrummy veggie stuff, as well as health food staples and coffee for which soya milk can be provided.

164

Clevedon

Located not far from Weston-Super-Mare, Clevedon is a charming Victorian seaside town. Unlike Weston's candy floss stalls, bright lights, amusement arcades and vast sandy beaches, Clevedon provides a more sedate – and for some more enjoyable – seaside trip.

Clevedon's pebbled shoreline is dominated by its Grade I listed pier – the only one of its kind in the country still intact. Off the beaten track, but still beside the sea, you will find some fantastic coastal walks which have inspired a host of famous poets and artists, including Tennyson. The Poet's Walk, named after such gifted individuals, has wonderful views across the Severn Estuary to the Welsh mountains. Perfect for blowing out the cobwebs.

In the summer you can enjoy a great day out on a boat trip from Clevedon to Holm Islands, Lundy Island, Minehead, Penarth or Watchet (visit www.waverleyexcursions.co.uk for details).

Tourist information

Visitor Information Centre

Clevedon Library, 37 Old Church Road, Clevedon BS21 6NN
Tel: 01275 873498 www.somersetcoast.com
Open: Monday, Thursday and Sunday 9.30am-5pm and
Tuesday and Friday 9.30am-7pm

Places to eat
Hill Road

Butterflies 🌱🌱

77 Hill Road, Clevedon BS21 7PL
Tel: 01275 872967
Opening times: Monday-Friday 9am-4.30pm and Saturday
8.30am-5pm
Veggie rating: 10% Vegetarian
Average cost: £4.00-£5.50
*As vegan choices are so limited in Clevedon I just had to flag
up that this nice little café does vegan flapjacks (although,
unfortunately, not all the time – unless of course you create
the demand!). For veggies there's more choice with a
selection of soups, paninis, rolls and cakes on the menu and
options such as Feta & Tomato Quiche with Salad.*

**Don't forget to mention the Vegetarian &
Vegan Guide to Bristol & Bath when making an
enquiry or booking!**

Junior Poon (Chinese Restaurant & Wine Bar) 🌓 ⑤ⓓ ⑩ ⑪
  16 Hill Road, Clevedon BS21 7NZ
  Tel: 01275 341900 www.juniorpoon.com
Opening times: Sunday-Friday midday-2pm and from 5.30pm
and Saturday midday-2pm and from 6.30pm
Veggie rating: 25% Vegetarian (vegan on request)
Average cost: Starters £5.50/Main courses £6.00
*This classy restaurant resides in a Grade II listed Georgian
building and has a private function room for bookings of up
to 46 people. The basement wine bar has a continental feel
and cosy atmosphere, with plush sofas and chairs to sink into
with your favourite tipple. Specialising in Peking and
Szechuan cuisine, there's some delicious veggie options
available, as well as two vegetarian set meals at
£19.00/£19.50. 20% discount for take-aways.*

Shops
Hill Road

Murrays (Delicatessen & Wine Shop)
  87 Hill Road, Clevedon BS21 7PN
  Tel: 01275 341222
Opening times: Tuesday-Saturday 8.30am-5pm
*Selling an extensive range of predominantly English and
Italian produce, this is a really nice deli, packed with lots of
goodies including Montezumas chocolate, fair-trade teas and
coffees, fresh fruit and veg, pasta, breads, preserves, olives,
oils, sun-dried tomatoes and more. The wine shop sells an
eclectic range of Italian wines, beers and other alcohol.*

Pullins (Bakery)

> *55 Hill Road, Clevedon BS21 7PD*
> *Tel: 01275 872974 www.pullinsbakers.co.uk*

Opening times: Monday-Friday 8.30am-4.30pm and Saturday 8.30am-4pm

Retail shop of family-run bakery, based in Yatton, which has been in business since 1925. All the breads are free from hydrogenated fats and there's some nice veggie and organic pasties, sandwiches, flapjacks and cakes, though sadly not vegan.

Rejuvenate (Health Foods & Therapy Rooms)

> *45 Hill Road, Clevedon BS21 7PD*
> *Tel: 01275 878200 www.rejuvenate.co.uk*

Opening times: Monday-Saturday 9.30am-5.30pm

As soon as you step into Rejuvenate you feel instantly relaxed. Whether it's the vibe or the soft scent of incense or candles, who knows, but it makes you feel good and it smells lovely! The shop has a well chosen selection of food and cleaning products as well as natural therapies, beauty products (including Herbatint hair dyes), bags, cards and music so a great place to come for some of your weekly shop as well as gifts.

Step downstairs into the therapy rooms and you enter a completely different space. The reception area is cool and calming, with a lovely cascading water feature and stylish and comfy sofas. Therapies include Deep Tissue Massage, Indian Head Massage, Colour Therapy and Reflexology to name but a few, with costs from £35.00 for an hour's treatment. Gift vouchers are available (and also for the shop).

Places to eat
Seafront

Little Harp Inn 🍷😊🌀🌀♿

Elton Road, Clevedon BS21 7RH
Tel: 01275 343739 www.littleharp-clevedon.com

Opening times: Monday-Saturday 10.30am-11pm and Sunday 11am-10.30pm (food served from midday-9pm)
Veggie rating: 27% Vegetarian; 0% Vegan
Music/vibe: Frank Sinatra, background
Average cost: Light bites £4.50/Main dishes £6.50

Formerly the gatekeeper's house to St Brandon's Estate, the Little Harp Inn overlooks the seafront, views of which you can enjoy from the patio. There's also a large beer garden where you can soak up the sun on warmer days. Vegans don't get a good deal unfortunately, but... there's always chips!

Places to eat
Town centre

Café Solo 😊○😊♿

22b Old Church Road, Clevedon BS21 6LY
Tel: 01275 873222

Opening times: Monday-Saturday 9am-4.30pm
Veggie rating: 48% Vegetarian; 0% Vegan
Average cost: Sandwiches £1.75-£2.50

Serving good honest grub, this café is one of the few in Clevedon that offers soya milk as well as a good selection of veggie options (albeit mostly cheese based). There's a function room available for hire and buffets can be provided on a small-scale. Warm and friendly, this place provides value for money.

La Bodega (Spanish Tapas Bar) 🅘 🅣🄰 🅘 🅢

  1 Old Street, Clevedon BS21 6ND
  Tel: 01275 871169 www.labodega.info

Opening times: Monday-Friday 9am-3pm and Saturday 9am-4pm

Veggie rating: 21% Vegetarian; 4% Vegan

Average cost: Paninis £3.25/Paella £7.50

If you're a bit of a paella fiend, then this is the place for you! As well as serving veggie paella to eat in or take away, La Bodega also sells paella making equipment so you can try your hand at recreating your favourite dish at home. It's not all paella though – there's also paninis, salads and Spanish omelettes too and, in the winter, vegan soup.

Monsoon (Indian) 🅞 🅑 🄶🄼 🅘 🅣🄰 🅢 🅢 🅖

  33 Old Church Road, Clevedon BS21 6NN
  Tel: 01275 340410

Opening times: Monday-Saturday midday-2pm and 5.30-11pm and Sunday midday-2pm and 5.30-10.30pm

Veggie rating: 12% Vegetarian (vegan on request)

Average cost: Starters £2.75/Main dishes £4.95

You can always rely on Indian cuisine to come up with the veggie goods and at Monsoon they certainly don't disappoint. Any of the vegetable side dishes can be made into a main dish which more than doubles the number of veggie options. Great! There's also a 10% discount on take-away orders over £6.00 so you can save your pennies when eating at home.

Tandoori Nights (Indian) 🌑🌑🌑🌑🌑🌑🌑

> *Unit 11, Clevedon Triangle Centre, Clevedon BS21 6HX*
> *Tel: 01275 342342*

Opening times: Monday-Sunday midday-2pm and 5.30pm-midnight

Veggie rating: 29% Vegetarian & Vegan

Average cost: Starters £2.95/Main dishes £5.95/Thali £8.95

This is a lovely place to go for a meal out, with curtained-off tables for extra privacy and a smart/casual dress code – so don't turn up in your flip flops, vest and shorts! Good food, good service and well-rated. 10% discount for take-away.

Shops

Holland & Barrett

> *6 Station Road, Clevedon BS21 6NH*
> *Tel: 01275 342049 www.hollandandbarrett.com*

Opening times: Monday-Saturday 9am-5.30pm

A health food haven for this part of town, which is a bit of a wasteland for veggies and especially vegans. There's just a small chiller cabinet with no take-away options but it does have vegan sausages, burgers etc and Swedish Glace dairy-free ice cream.

Souk

> *The Triangle, Clevedon BS21 6NB*
> *Tel: 01275 340002 www.radiosol.com/souk*

Opening times: Monday-Saturday 9.15am-5pm

This is a lovely little shop which packs a lot in for its size, including some beautiful clothes, jewellery, bags and home furnishings as well as soaps, incense etc. Souk support independent craftspeople where possible and only buy items that are not sold by any other outlet in the area so you can pick up something unique and affordable.

© Rob Hill

Weston-Super-Mare's Grand Pier

Weston-Super-Mare

"Oh, I do like to be beside the seaside....Oh, I do like to be beside the sea..." If you're looking for the archetypal seaside town, you've certainly come to the right place! Everything you love and expect to see is here – a huge sandy beach perfect for building sandcastles, a pier to stroll along and feel the cool sea breeze in your hair (as well as the candy floss which always seems to get stuck to mine!), amusement arcades, gardens*, chip shops and cafés serving up seaside staples of pies, peas and chips and unfortunately a small army of donkeys to carry visitors up and down the beach all day.

For many, particularly families, Weston-Super-Mare is a great place to come, especially in the holidays, and for vegetarians and vegans there's a surprisingly good selection on offer, especially if you go beyond the seafront and head into town. There's more to Weston-Super-Mare than pies, peas and chips, I promise, so what are you waiting for? Come in, the water's... freezing!

Jill's Garden in Grove Park was created by the BBC Ground Force team in memory of the late TV presenter Jill Dando. Tel 01934 888800 for details.

Don't forget to mention the Vegetarian & Vegan Guide to Bristol & Bath when making an enquiry or booking!

Tourist information

Tourist Information Centre

Beach Lawns, Weston-Super-Mare BS23 1AT
Tel: 01934 888800 www.somersetcoast.com
Open: Summer: Monday-Saturday 9.30am-5pm; Winter:
Monday-Friday 10am-5pm and Saturday 9.30am-4pm

Places to stay

Beachlands Hotel (3 Star) ⭕ 🅥 🌓 🆂🅳 🅖🅜 ✇ ✇ ♿ 🅿

17 Uphill Road North, Weston-Super-Mare BS23 4NG
Tel: 01934 621401 www.beachlandshotel.com
Open: Year round, except 10 days over Christmas
Number of rooms: 24 **En-suite**: 24
Cost: £59.50-£79.50 per person per night
Views: Some rooms overlook the golf course
Veggie breakfast: Cooked breakfast
Vegan breakfast: Available on request
If you're a golf lover, this hotel will be perfect for you as it overlooks the golf course. But, for the golf widows and people like me that just aren't interested in the sport, don't worry as it's also just a 200 yard stroll from the beach too. And it has an indoor heated pool and sauna – bliss! About a quarter of the hotel's restaurant menu is veggie so you won't even need to set foot outside to satisfy your hunger pangs.

Corbiere Hotel (3 Diamond) ⚪🆜🟢

24 Upper Church Road, Weston-Super-Mare BS23 2DX
Tel: 01934 629607 www.corbierehotel.co.uk

Open: Year round
Number of rooms: 9 **En-suite**: 9
Cost: £20.00-£26.00 per person per night
Veggie breakfast: Cooked breakfast: sausages, egg, mushrooms, beans, tomato & toast
Vegan breakfast: As above without sausages & egg

Tuck into some tasty home-cooked food in the dining room, or relax in the lounge, enjoying views of the lovely garden which has won the Weston Tourism Flower Power Award 2004/5. Soya milk and other dairy-free products are available on request, as are evening meals. Blooming lovely!

New Ocean Hotel (AA 2 Star) ⚪🟠🆜🟢🟢🟢🟢🅿

26 Burnbeck Road, Madeira Cove,
Weston-Super-Mare BS23 2BS
Tel: 01934 621839 www.newoceanhotel.co.uk

Open: Year round, except January
Number of rooms: 53 **En-suite**: 53
Cost: £35 per person per night
Views: 20 rooms overlooking Marine Lake
Veggie breakfast: Fruit; Cereal; Toast; English breakfast
Vegan breakfast: Available on request

Family-run hotel located on the seafront opposite Marine Lake. The restaurant uses local produce where possible so food miles are kept to a minimum. After dark they offer traditional entertainment and you can boogie the night away on the dance floor. As David Bowie said "Let's dance!".

Oakover Guest House (4 Star, Sparkling Diamond)

25 Clevedon Road, Weston-Super-Mare BS23 1DA
Tel: 01934 620125 www.oakover.co.uk

Open: Year round
Number of rooms: 6 **En-suite**: 6
Cost: From £24.00 per person per night
Veggie breakfast: Fresh fruit; Yoghurts; Cereals; Toast &
preserves; Cooked breakfast
Vegan breakfast: Available on request

Family-run guest house handily positioned just two minutes
from the seafront and five or so minutes from town. A
number of luxury double bedrooms are available, as well as
standard rooms, which are really something special – perfect
for a romantic weekend away.

Weston Bay Hotel (3 Diamond)

2-4 Clevedon Road, Weston-Super-Mare BS23 1DG
Tel: 01934 628903 www.westonbayhotel.co.uk

Open: March-November
Number: 9 **En-suite**: 9
Cost: £30 per person per night
Views: Five rooms have a sea view
Veggie breakfast: Cooked breakfast
Vegan breakfast: Available on request

Also on the seafront, the family-run and Victorian Weston
Bay Hotel has views of Weston Beach Lawns, the promenade
and the bay. Holiday flats (one bedroom) are also available
adjacent to the hotel.

Places to eat

Ama Café (English/Bosnian) ⬤🞄🞄🞄🞄

12 The Centre, Weston-Super-Mare BS23 1UW
Tel: 01934 644348

Opening times: Monday-Sunday 10am-10pm
Veggie rating: 10% Vegetarian; 3% Vegan
Average cost: Main dishes £4.95

Serving the usual English fare, this nice and surprisingly capacious café opposite the Town Hall is unusual in that it also serves a full range of Bosnian cuisine, much of which is veggie. Dishes include Musaka (potato slices & aubergines with soya mince) or Leca Lesanja (lentil lasagne).

Bengal Raj Restaurant & Take-Away (Bangladeshi) ⬤🞄🞄🞄🞄🞄🞄🞄🞄

18 The Boulevard, Weston-Super-Mare BS23 1NA
Tel: 01934 625838 www.bengalraj.com

Opening times: Monday-Sunday midday-2pm and 6pm-midnight
Veggie rating: 10% Vegetarian; 5% Vegan
Music/vibe: Indian
Average cost: Starters £2.10/Main dishes £4.50

If you fancy a change then the Bengal Raj has some lovely choices, including Nobabi Niramishi – which is roasted potatoes with cauliflower, peas & mushrooms, cooked in a rich creamy sauce of coconut milk, almonds & coconut with very mild spices and fresh herbs – and Labra – aubergines, bendy & spinach cooked in a spicy tangy sauce of lentils. The real thing and great value, with 10% off for take-aways over £10.00, it's the biz.

Costa @ Ottakers ● ●

Units 21-23, The Sovereign Centre,
Weston-Super-Mare BS23 1HL
Tel: 01934 417529 www.costa.co.uk

Opening times: Monday, Wednesday-Saturday 9am-5pm,
Tuesday 9.30am-5pm and Sunday 10.30am-4pm
One of the few places that offers soya milk in Weston and a
handy place to take five after a shopping spree!

The Curry Garden Tandoori Restaurant
● ● ● ● ●

69 Orchard Street, Weston-Super-Mare BS23 1RL
Tel: 01934 624660

Opening hours: Monday-Thursday and Sunday midday-2pm
and 6pm-midnight and Friday-Saturday midday-2pm, 6pm-
12.30am
Veggie rating: 30% Vegetarian & Vegan
Music/vibe: Indian instrumental
Average cost: Starters £2.50/Main dishes £5.00
Apparently The Curry Garden is the oldest Indian restaurant
in Weston and has over the years earned a reputation for its
great food and friendly staff. There's a wide range of veggie
dishes on offer as well as a set meal for just £6.80 and
apparently any dish can be prepared to order – so why not
put them to the test?!

Delaneys Sandwich Bar

1 Alexandra Parade, Weston-Super-Mare BS23 1QS
Tel: 01934 637777

Opening hours: Monday-Friday 8am-2pm and Saturday
8am-1pm
Veggie rating: 25% Vegetarian (vegan on request)

Average cost: £1.50-£2.50

A nice little take-away offering freshly prepared sandwiches, baguettes, wraps, jackets and salads. Dairy-free mayonnaise and Parmezano are available on request. Good value for money.

Fudds Restaurant (Anglo/French)

◐⊙⟨⟩⓪◎⊗⊗⊗⊛

> *73 Meadow Street, Weston-Super-Mare BS23 1QL*
> *Tel: 01934 629973 www.fudds.co.uk*

Opening hours: Monday-Thursday 9am-5pm and Friday-Saturday 9am-late

Veggie rating: 50% Vegetarian (vegan on request)

Music/vibe: Easy listening

Average cost: Main dishes £4.25 daytime/£7.50 evening

This stylish restaurant offers good options for veggies on both its daytime and evening menus. Fill lunchtime pangs with a sandwich of roasted red pepper, sun-dried tomato & salad and, by night, Spinach & Mushroom Risotto. If you can get a large enough group of friends and family, why not book a private taster night?

Great Wall (Chinese/Thai Take-Away) ⓥ⊗

> *7 The Centre, Weston-Super-Mare BS23 1US*
> *Tel: 01934 620022*

Opening hours: Sunday-Thursday 5-11pm and Friday-Saturday 5pm-midnight

Veggie rating: 25% Vegetarian & Vegan

Average cost: Main dishes £3.00

Grab a taste of the Orient to go! There's some delicious dishes to sink your teeth into, such as the Mixed Vegetables in Coconut Sauce or Beancurd with Garlic Black Bean Sauce.

And, if you really want to have a feast, the Vegetarian Set Meal for One should well and truly fill you up!

Heritage Coffee House ⊖☾◑◙☙

3 Wadham Street, Weston-Super-Mare BS23 1JY
Tel: 01934 626402

Opening times: Monday-Saturday 9.30am-4.30pm
Veggie rating: 99% Vegetarian; 10% Vegan
Music/vibe: Classic FM
Average cost: Salads £3.00-£4.00/Main dishes £5.75

Part of the Heritage Centre which was built in 1895-96 and restored as a meeting place of the Weston Civic Society, the coffee house started out life as a coach house for the riding stables next door. Now it has a lovely country kitchen feel, with large wooden tables and chairs and stone flooring. Proud of its veggie clientele and boasting that vegetarian and wholefoods are a speciality, it's disappointing that soya milk or many vegan options are missing from the menu. But nor are there many meat options, just veggie and fish in a number of guises including jacket potatoes, omelettes, ploughmans, salads and sandwiches. There's a good selection of hot and cold drinks including Pukka herbal teas and beers with which you can wash down a Hummus Jacket Potato (vegan), Mozzarella & Sun-dried Tomato Ciabatta or even Honey & Banana Sandwich!

Don't forget to mention the Vegetarian & Vegan Guide to Bristol & Bath when making an enquiry or booking!

Hot Cuisine (Indian, English & Exotic)

⊘ ⊕ ◎ ⊘ ⊘ ⊕

22-26 St James Street, Weston-Super-Mare BS23 1ST
Tel: 01934 633884 www.hotcuisine.co.uk

Opening times: Monday-Sunday midday-2.30pm and 5.30-11.30pm

Veggie rating: 15% Vegetarian; 5% Vegan

Music/vibe: Contemporary

Average cost: Starters £2.95/Main dishes £5.95

With helpful (and scary) ratings from 1-10 for the strength of dishes, this huge restaurant offers three menus – Indian, Exotic and English – and many veggie options. And while you wait for your meal to be whisked to your table, you can watch your food being cooked on CCTV monitors. Thumbs down: for the poor parrot that's stuck in a cage by the window. Featured in their promo, you'll see him looking noticeably perkier than he does in real life.

Juicy Bits (Juice Bar) ⊘ ⊜ ⓐ ⊕

14 West Street, Weston-Super-Mare BS23 1JT
Tel: 01934 637770

Opening times: Monday-Saturday 10am-4pm

Veggie rating: 20% Vegetarian; 5% Vegan

Average cost: Sandwiches £1.60-£1.80/Panini £2.00

Hasn't got quite the vibe of most juice bars and surprised that soya milk isn't on offer but the choice of freshly squeezed juices and smoothies is good. There's also paninis, salad bowls, jacket potatoes, burgers, sandwiches and baguettes on offer, with veggie options for each. There's some seating available so you can hang or eat on the go.

Number One (Patisserie Café) ⓥⓖ❶🟠🟢🟢♿

1 The Boulevard, Weston-Super-Mare BS23 1NN
Tel: 01934 614416

Opening times: Monday-Friday 8am-5pm (and 6-11pm Friday), Saturday 9.30am-4.30pm and 6-11pm, and Sunday 9.30am-3.00pm

Veggie rating: 10% Vegetarian (vegan on request)

Music/vibe: Soft background

Average cost: Lunch £5.00-£6.00/Dinner £15.00-£20.00

A classy little place offering some nice veggie options like Seasonal Stuffed Mushrooms or Goat's Cheese & Roasted Vegetable Tart. All dishes are freshly prepared so can be adapted for vegans. On a nice day, you can sit outside and watch the world – and lots of traffic! – go by.

Sea Palace Oriental Restaurant ❶🟠🆃🟢🟢🟢♿

35-39 St James Street, Weston-Super-Mare BS23 1ST
Tel: 01934 626262

Opening times: Monday-Thursday midday-2.30pm and 6-11pm and Friday-Saturday midday-2.30pm and 6pm-midnight

Veggie rating: 15% Vegetarian & Vegan

Music/vibe: Easy listening

Average cost: Starters £3.50-£5.00/Main dishes £6.00-£7.00

Offering some nice veggie options, this upmarket restaurant offers a 15% discount when ordering take-away. Try the Lettuce Wrap or Vermicilli Singapore Style or the Vegetarian Set Menu at £14.95. Just ensure that the stock will be vegetable, not meat, based when ordering!

Shake Shack ⬤⬤🅰

57 Regent Street, Weston-Super-Mare BS23 1SP
Tel: 0845 838 2686

Opening times: Monday-Sunday 10am-7pm
Average cost: Regular £2.10/Large £3.10 (add 50p for organic milk)

It's great that these shake places are springing up all over the place, especially as they offer soya milk and vegan options. 10% discount available for students.

Tarantella Ristorante Pizzeria ❶⬤⬤⬤⬤

29-31 St James Street, Weston-Super-Mare BS23 1ST
Tel: 01934 620701

Opening times: Tuesday-Saturday midday-2.30pm and 5.30-11pm and Sunday midday-2.30pm
Veggie rating: 23% Vegetarian (vegan on request)
Music/vibe: Radio
Average cost: Main dishes £4.50/Pizza £7.55

Italian restaurants are a great place to get veggie options and this family-run one is no exception. Pizza lovers (and who isn't?) can tuck into the Pizza Vegetariana or for something a little bit different there's the Mannata Di Legumi alla Griglia (that's chargrilled aubergines, courgettes & peppers marinated in olive oil, mint, chilli & garlic with salad and mozzarella to you and me — vegans can just say hold the cheese).

Tiffins Coffee House (Traditional English)
⬤⬤⬤⬤⬤⬤⬤⬤⬤⬤⬤

Purn Way, Bleadon, Weston-Super-Mare BS24 0AE
Tel: 01934 815582

Opening times: Monday-Friday 8.30am-4pm, Saturday 9am-4pm and Sunday 9am-1pm

Veggie rating: 30% Vegetarian; 2% Vegan

Average cost: Starters £2.50/Main courses £3.50/Desserts £1.75

Situated on the West Mendip Way in an area of outstanding natural beauty, Tiffins is linked to the Bleadon Post Office & Country Stores. Local produce is used where possible for their menu which includes Veggie Breakfast Platter, Roasted Vegetables with Mozzarella & Pesto Sauce Panini and, for vegans, good old Jacket Potato with Beans.

Toogies ⬤⬤⬤⬤⬤⬤⬤

30-32 The Boulevard, Weston-Super-Mare BS23 1NF
Tel: 01934 623639

Opening times: Monday-Saturday 8am-4pm and Sunday 9am-3pm

Veggie rating: 50% Vegetarian; 15% Vegan

Music/vibe: Radio

Average cost: Main dishes £4.00-£6.00/Desserts £1.85

A no-nonsense and spacious café, this place does a great Veggie Breakfast of hash browns, bubble & squeak, onion rings, veggie sausage, mushrooms, grilled tomatoes, beans & toast. Phew – if that doesn't sort you out, nothing will! If you're of a more delicate disposition you can opt for the pick 'n' mix breakfast where you can choose any five items with toast for just £2.99. They also do Veggie Sausage in Onion Gravy with Chips & Peas.

Shops

Boulevard Pharmacy

23 Waterloo Street, Weston-Super-Mare BS23 1LF
Tel: 01934 628845

Opening times: Monday-Saturday 9.30am-5.30pm (closed 1-2pm Saturday)

It's always useful to know where the nearest chemist is but it's even better to know about this one as not only is it packed with all the usual suspects (products not punters!), but there's also a wonderfully wide range of natural therapies, flower remedies and toiletries.

The Chinese Medicine Shop

26 High Street, Weston-Super-Mare BS23 1JF
Tel: 01934 621828

Opening times: Monday-Saturday 9am-5.30pm

It's not unusual these days to find a herbalist in most towns, and Weston is no different other than it boasts two! Pop in to find a host of herbal remedies for everyday ailments.

The Co-op

20 Oxford Street, Weston-Super-Mare BS23 1TF
Tel: 01934 417889

Opening times: Monday-Sunday 7am-10pm

The Co-op is a great friend to those on the go as you know that wherever you find one you can also find cruelty-free and vegan toiletries, not to mention a good selection of vegan wines and fair-trade products, which are clearly labelled.

Dr China

> Unit 36, The Sovereign Centre, High Street,
> Weston-Super-Mare BS23 1HL
> Tel: 01934 628862

Opening times: Monday-Saturday 9am-5.30pm and Sunday 11am-4.30pm

Like the Chinese Medicine Shop on the High Street (see previous), Dr China offers lots of herbal remedies as well as acupuncture treatments. Just pop in to talk through your ailment and they'll come up with a natural solution.

Fudds Deli

> 49 Meadow Street, Weston-Super-Mare BS23 1QJ
> Tel: 01934 644066

Opening times: Monday-Saturday 8am-4pm

Quality food freshly prepared, with an emphasis on local and organic. Offering take out sandwiches (vegans can enjoy hummus with sun-dried tomato & green olives on wholemeal baguette for example) and hot drinks (including Green & Black's hot chocolate), this great little place also sells lots of lovely things to eat (olives, chutneys, jams) as well as the Ecover range and vegan candles.

Holland & Barrett

> 19 Meadow Street, Weston-Super-Mare BS23 1QG
> Tel: 01934 620020 www.hollandandbarrett.com

Opening times: Monday-Saturday 9.30am-5.30pm and Sunday 10am-4pm

When you find a Holland & Barrett you know you'll be able to stock up on veggie staples and the Weston store is a good size with a chiller cabinet (so you can buy ready-to-eat pies and pasties as well as vegan cheeses, yoghurts and frozen

products), as well as all the usual nibbles of nuts, dried fruits, flapjacks and more.

The Java Lounge (Internet Café)

38-40 Orchard Street, Weston-Super-Mare BS23 1RH
Tel: 01934 647868

Opening times: Monday-Friday 10am-10pm and Saturday 10am-8pm

Not much in the way of food and drink available here but useful to know for those wanting to hook up with friends and family.

Julian Graves

Unit 9, The Sovereign Centre, Weston-Super-Mare BS23 1HL
Tel: 01934 643144 www.juliangraves.com

Opening times: Monday-Saturday 9am-5.30pm and Sunday 10.30am-4.30pm

Another high street regular, Julian Graves is packed to the gunnels with all sorts of nuts and fruits for you to nibble on as well as various sweet treats including the deliciously soft Australian Black Opal liquorice.

Oxfam

9 West Street, Weston-Super-Mare BS23 1JR
Tel: 01934 415335

Opening times: Monday-Saturday 9.30am-5pm

It's always good to have a rifle through the second-hand book selection at Oxfam, as well as clothes and general bits and bobs, but you can also buy an increasingly wide range of fair-trade products from coffee and hot chocolate to dried fruits and the delicious Divine chocolate range.

Pippin Harris

1 Kewstoke Road, Kewstoke, Weston-Super-Mare BS22 9YB
Tel: 01934 642269 www.pippinharris.co.uk

Opening times: Monday-Saturday 9am-5pm and Sunday 11am-4.30pm

Farm shop selling a wide range of British products from fruit and veg to teas, coffees, juices etc both from its stores in Portishead (see page 94) and Weston-Super-Mare as well as online. Local suppliers are used where possible and many products are grown to organic standards, although may not be certificated as such.

The Willow Tree

62 Meadow Street, Weston-Super-Mare BS23 1QJ
Tel: 01934 633935

Opening times: Monday-Saturday 9.30am-5pm

If you fancy a change from the screaming kids and fast food kiosks, seek sanctuary at The Willow Tree. There's plenty to bring your pulse down to a soothing saunter including incense sticks, candles, books, gifts and gems.

Ye Old Rock & Candy Shop

4 Regent Street, Weston-Super-Mare BS23 1SQ
Tel: 01934 641180

Opening times: Monday-Saturday 9.30am-6pm and Sunday 10am-6pm (seasonal variations may apply)

You can't visit the seaside without getting a bag of something sweet and sticky and here you can do just that! Treat yourself to a bumper bag of honeycomb which is not only absolutely yummy but vegan too. If you can save some for home why not go to the next level and pour melted chocolate on for a truly sweet treat!

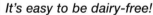

Other

There's some fantastic places beyond Bristol and Bath – Avebury, Cheddar Gorge, Glastonbury and Wells to name but a few – with an array of wonderful countryside and historical buildings to explore (not to mention the fantastic spectacle of the mass starling roost at West Hay near Glastonbury each winter). So if you fancy a day trip or afternoon out, the following veggie-friendly places are well worth a visit.

Glastonbury Tor

© Simon Parkin

Avebury

The Circle Restaurant ⊖⊘⊛⊛⊘⊕⊕⊖⊛⊛⊛

National Trust, Avebury SN8 1RF
Tel: 01672 539514

Opening times: Summer: Monday-Sunday 10am-6.30pm;
Winter: Monday-Sunday 10am-3.30pm
Veggie rating: 100% Vegetarian; 20% Vegan
Average cost: Main dishes £6.95/Desserts £1.00-£2.25
*Long-standing veggie restaurant, now run by the National
Trust, which is just a stone's throw from the striking Avebury
stones. Opposite the National Trust shop, with outdoor
seating too, the café serves a range of sandwiches, hot
dishes and cakes. Sadly, the atmosphere isn't quite what
you'd expect and hope for at such an amazing location –
there's a canteen feel about the place – which is a shame.
Vegan options are clearly marked although get there early
to ensure that there's still some chocolate cake left!*

Cheddar Gorge

Bay Rose House B&B (4 Diamond)
⊖⊖⊘⊛⊛⊛⊛⊛⊛⊛⊛

Cheddar Gorge BS27 3QN
Tel: 01934 741377 www.bayrose.co.uk

Open: Year round
Number of rooms: 3 **En-suite**: 3
Cost: £60.00 (double), £40.00 (single) per room per night
Veggie breakfast: Cereals; Fruit; Bread/muffins; Porridge;
Cooked breakfast or Marmite eggs florentine

Vegan breakfast: Available on request
A 19th Century English country cottage set at the foot of the fantastic Cheddar Gorge, Bay Rose is the perfect place to unwind and get away from it all.

Devizes

The Healthy Life & Bistro (Restaurant, Private Dining Room, Cookery School & Natural Food Store)
🌑🌑🌑🌑🌑🌑🌑🌑🌑🌑🌑

> *4-7 Little Brittox, Devizes SN10 1AR*
> *Tel: 01380 725558 www.thehealthylife.co.uk*

Opening times: Restaurant: Tuesday-Saturday 10am-3pm and 7pm-late. Store: Monday-Saturday 9am-5.30pm
Veggie rating: Day-time: 75% Vegetarian; 50% Vegan, Evening: 40% Vegetarian; 25% Vegetarian
Music/vibe: Easy listening
Average cost: Day-time: Main courses £6.95/Desserts £4.95, Evening: 2 courses £18.95/3 courses £22.95
The Healthy Life is a real godsend providing not just good wholesome food in its restaurant, but also via its private dining room – where owner Peter Vaughan will cook for you and up to 25 friends – cookery school and natural food store. These people like to keep busy! Meals are produced using local produce, organic and fairly traded where possible, as well as ingredients from the store, and are nutritionally and naturally balanced.

Frome

The Garden Café (World) ⬤⬤⬤⬤⬤⬤⬤⬤⬤⬤⬤⬤⬤

16 Stony Street, Frome BA11 1BU
Tel: 01373 454178 www.gardencafefrome.co.uk

Opening times: Monday-Wednesday 9am-5.30pm, Thursday-
Saturday 9am-late and Sunday 10.30am-4pm

Veggie rating: 100% Vegetarian; 10% Vegan

Music/vibe: World/folk/ambient

Average cost: Starters £4.00/Main dishes £7.00/Desserts £3.00

*Frome's only natural, vegetarian and organic café, The
Garden Café has several cosy eating areas including a
sheltered courtyard garden from which to enjoy its
wholesome delights. On offer there's toasted sandwiches,
main dishes including Cashew Nut & Bean Patties served with
Salad, Pitta & Yoghurt (which can be veganised) and Halloumi
Cheese & Marinaded Vegetable Kebabs and a selection of
cakes and pastries. And for those that enjoy a tipple there's a
good choice of wines, ciders, beers and spirits – all of which
are organic AND vegan! There's also a children's menu and
on some evenings you can enjoy live music or poetry.*

Frome Wholefoods

8 Cheap Street, Frome BA11 1BN
Tel: 01373 473334

Opening times: Monday-Wednesday and Friday 9.30am-
5.30pm, Thursday 9.30am-5pm and Saturday 9am-5pm

*This is a great little wholefood shop selling a wide variety of
products for its size, including cakes and other take-away options
and some chilled and frozen vegan products that you might not
easily find in similar shops. Well worth a visit if in town.*

Glastonbury

The Lightship ⊖ ∅

82 Bove Town, Glastonbury BA6 8JG
Tel: 01458 833698 www.lightship.ukf.net

Open: Year-round
Number of rooms: 2
Veggie breakfast: Fruit fruit; Cereals; Organic mushroom, tomato, egg & veggie sausages; Organic wholemeal toast & preserves
Vegan breakfast: As above

The Lightship is a mediaeval town house from 1390, formerly a hostelry for pilgrims to Glastonbury Abbey. Guests can enjoy the Turkish tea-garden by lamplight and stargazing roof room with telescope and amazing views of Glastonbury Tor. As well as B&B, The Lightship can also be let on a self-catering basis.

Rainbows End Café ⊖ ⊘ ⊛ ⊛ ⑳ ◍ ⊜ ⑭ ⊛

17A High Street, Glastonbury BA6 9DP
Tel: 01458 833896

Opening times: Monday-Sunday 10am-4pm
Veggie rating: 100% Vegetarian; 35% Vegan
Average cost: Main dishes £6.00-£7.00/Cakes £1.50-£3.00

On the high street but tucked away up a short corridor behind a shop, this is the best place to eat in town and fantastic value for money. Choose from a lovely selection of salads, which you can have with a slice of quiche or veggie bake, as well as flapjacks and cakes and a good range of hot and cold drinks, many of which are organic. You get very good portions, so much so that you might want to share, especially the super iced slabs of cakes they do which are perfect for the sweet tooth!

The Bridget Healing Centre 🍏

The Courtyard, 2-4 High Street, Glastonbury BA6 9DU
Tel: 01458 833317 www.bridgethealingcentre.co.uk

Opening times: Summer: Monday-Friday 10am-5pm; Winter: Monday-Friday 11am-4pm

The longest running healing and complementary centre in Glastonbury, The Bridget Healing Centre offers visitors a wide range of therapies for the body, mind and soul. Choose from the more conventional alternative therapies of Acupuncture and Reflexology to the more unusual Dream Readings and Shamanic Healing. Viva! supporters can take advantage of a 10% discount on treatments provided by therapist Yvonne Fields.

The Wholefood Store 🍏

29 High Street, Glastonbury BA6 9DR
Tel: 01458 831004

Opening times: Monday-Saturday 9am-5.30pm and Sunday 11am-5pm

A good-sized and well-stocked independent health food shop that's thankfully open on a Sunday too! You can find all your essentials here as well as organic wines, dairy-free chocs and more, including green magazines and a great range of remedies and bodycare products.

Don't forget to mention the Vegetarian & Vegan Guide to Bristol & Bath when making an enquiry or booking!

Wells

Canon Grange House (4 Star) ⊖⊘⊘⊘⊛

Cathedral Green, Wells BA5 2UB
Tel: 01749 671800 www.canongrange.co.uk

Open: Year round
Number of rooms: 5 **En-suite**: 4
Cost: £52.00-£68.00 per room per night
Views: Two with views of cathedral
Veggie breakfast: Fresh fruit salad & yoghurt; Selection of cereals; Toast; Cooked breakfast: for example fresh mushrooms on toast, with beans, Quorn pâté, vegetarian sausages, sweetcorn & tomatoes
Vegan breakfast: Available on request

Enjoy 16th century elegance with 21st century comfort at the Canon Grange House, which is in a splendid location in the centre of Wells on Cathedral Green. Many of the bedrooms are spacious with exposed beams and tasteful furnishings, and two have wonderful views of the West Front of Wells cathedral. A great place to explore Wells from.

The Good Earth (Restaurant & Shop)
⊖⊛⊛⊙⊜⊘⊘⊛

4 Priory Road, Wells BA5 1SY
Tel: 01749 678600

Opening times: Monday-Saturday 9am-5pm
Veggie rating: 100% Vegetarian; 35% Vegan
Average cost: Main dishes £4.95/Desserts £2.95

Nice combo of veggie café and shop selling health foods, established for over 25 years. The café has lots of seating and plenty of nooks and crannies to seek refuge in and the hearty food is good value.

Wrington

The Walled Garden Café & Shop
😊😊😊😊🚹🚺😶😊😊😊😊😊♿

Barley Wood, Long Lane, Wrington BS40 5SA
Tel: 01934 863713

Opening times: Monday-Sunday 9.30am-4.30pm and Friday-Saturday from 7pm (café only)

Veggie rating: 50% Vegetarian; 10% Vegan

Music/vibe: Classical

Average cost: Starters £5.20/Main dishes £11.95-£15.95/Desserts £5.20

The Walled Garden and its café and shop is run by The Better Food Co (see page 106). The café is a delightful place to eat, especially on a long summer's evening, as it overlooks the garden and the surrounding countryside. Menu options include mains of Cream of Celeriac Soup or Courgette, Red Onion & Goat's Cheese Tart and desserts of Apple Crumble or Brownie with Warm Chocolate Sauce. The garden has a history dating back to 1901 when it was owned by the director of Imperial Tobacco Company. Over the years it changed hands and fell into neglect, until it was purchased by its current owner in 1993, who replanted fruit trees etc to replicate how it would've been at the turn of the century. In 2002, Better Food took over production of the fruit and veg, providing produce for its box scheme, supermarket in Bristol and local restaurants and shops. Visitors to the café and shop can look round the garden for a small fee (April-October: £2.50 Adult, £2.00 Concession/Child; November-March: £1.00, under 14s free).

A quick guide to veggie booze

Trying to find out whether eateries serve vegetarian or vegan alcohol can be fraught, as most staff haven't a clue and aren't even aware that wines, beers and other alcohol could be anything but veggie! It is made from fruit, after all. Little do they know!

The key problem isn't so much what goes into the drink, it's what doesn't come out and what's used during the production process.

Wines

Most wines, and port and sherry for that matter, have been fined using one or more animal products, and some pretty grim ones at that. You wouldn't be saying cheers if you knew you were toasting with a glass of vino made using blood or bone, chitin (crustacean) or gelatine (boiled animal tissues), fish oils or isinglass (from the air bladders of fish), as well as egg albumen or milk.

Knowledgeable eateries will know which of their wines are veggie, and stock them in the first place, so do ask. If they don't know, your enquiry will make them more aware and hopefully more pro-active in ensuring there's a good veggie choice.

For home dining, it's quite easy to find animal-free alternatives – the Co-op does a very good range, including fair-trade, with vegetarian and vegan wines clearly marked. Shops such as Fresh & Wild and Harvest, and other independent health food stores, also stock some lovely veggie wines so check them out. And you don't even have to set foot outside – you can join Viva!'s very own Wine Club

from the comfort of your home – simply call 0117 944 1000
or visit www.viva.org.uk/shop for details.

Beers

The use of animal ingredients in the production of beers depends
on the type of beer. For example, 'real ales' are generally fined
using isinglass, as is Stella Artois and some lagers. Keg, canned
and some bottled beers are usually okay, although for these and
other beers, an animal-derived additive may be used.

The following beers are – to the best of our knowledge –
animal-free, although if unsure, it may be best to check with
the manufacturers:

Beck's	Grolsch	Kingfisher
Brugs	Heineken Export	Lowenbrau Pils
Budweiser	Hoegaarden	Mort Subite
Carlsberg	Holsten Pils	Rolling Rock
Grimbergen	Judas	

as well as the following Charles Wells Beers (Can, Bottle, Keg
not Cask) – Banana Bread Beer, Bombardier Bitter, Cobra
Lager, Eagle Bitter, Kirin Lager and Red Stripe.

Ciders

Most ciders have been fined with gelatine, but it's not all
bad news, scrumpy-type ciders are likely to be okay.

Spirits

Most spirits are suitable for veggies, although give Malt
Whisky, some blended whiskies and Spanish brandies a wide
berth, as well as imported vodkas, which may have been
filtered through bone charcoal.

Index
Places to stay

Places to eat

Shops etc

Notes

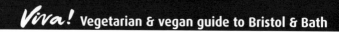

Notes

Notes

BECAUSE BEING A MAN MEANS MORE THAN HAVING MEAT AND TWO VEG

Men and women rejoice; being veggie is about enjoying the best things in life and there's plenty of passion in the compassionate. As shown by gold medal winning athletes, academics, popstars and gorgeous models alike, an animal free diet is perfect for the animals, the environment and your health.

Factory farming abuses animals on a massive scale and is destroying the planet, which is why Viva! is doing all it can to end it. With your support, we can be even more effective.

YES, I want to join *Viva!*

Tick here to join as a: ❏ Supporter – £15 (waged)
❏ Supporter – £12 (unwaged)
❏ Star Supporter – £25* Tick if prefer ❏ video or ❏ DVD

Supporters receive the highly acclaimed *Viva!Life* magazine three times a year – also a free car sticker and Supporter's Card. As well as all the above, Star Supporters receive the *Not In My Name* celebrity video or DVD*, six *Viva!* Guides and a *Viva!* brooch and sticker.

Title: .... First Name: .... Surname: ....

Address: ....

.... Postcode: ....

Tel: ....

I enclose a cheque/PO (payable to *Viva!*) for £ ....
OR Please debit my Visa/Mastercard/Solo/Switch:

Expires: .... Start date/issue no: .... Signature: ....

Please post today to: *Viva!*, 8 York Court, Wilder Street, Bristol BS2 8QH. OR join or donate by phone on *0117 944 1000* (Mon-Fri, 9am-6pm) or online at *www.viva.org.u*